"mother at the wheel"

Lise Norgaard

MOTHER

AT THE

WHEEL

translated by
Carl Blechingberg
cover art and illustrations by
Kamma Svensson

Taplinger Publishing Company
New York 1963

First English Language Edition Published by Taplinger Publishing Co., Inc., January, 1963
Copyright © 1962 by Taplinger Publishing Co., Inc.
Published simultaneously in Canada by Burns & MacEachern, Ltd., Toronto
First printing
Library of Congress Catalog Card Number: 62-17897
Designed by Wladislaw Finne
Printed in the United States of America

"mother at the wheel"

chapter I ...

*. . . relating how my mother mounted
the barricades to enable her to seize
the wheel— and how she
relinquished it again.*

One of the greatest riddles in the history of motoring is connected with my mother's acquisition of a driving license. I am well aware that research workers investigating other phenomena connected with automobiles will be able to tell of happenings that baffle explanation. There are, no doubt, stories of cars that have disappeared at sea or in the jungle, of cars that found their own way home, perhaps even of cars that found parking space in the center of Copenhagen between the hours of two and four in the afternoon. But if the story of my mother's enrollment in the ranks of practicing motorists nevertheless surpasses other accounts of incomprehensible character, it is because the mystery leaves two questions unanswered.

Question One: How did mother manage to pass the driving test? Question Two: How is it that so few lives were lost while mother was at the wheel?

Before I put my Pegasus in third gear and introduce the gentle reader to my mother's career as a motorist

I must give a first-gear account of my father's cars and his relationship to these.

My father was a motoring pioneer. At an early stage he foresaw the rich possibilities inherent in this newfangled method of transport, especially for the noble youth desiring to bring himself advantageously to the notice of the fair sex. His first car was an orgy of shining brass and lacquer, and so small as to allow room for himself and a charming young lady only. Long before the men of the advertising profession realized the decorative effect of a blonde in the front seat, my father had launched this innovation.

My mother was the blondest girl in town, and her green eyes magnificently matched the green lacquer of his 1918 Renault, as did her ash-blonde hair the brass fittings. There seemed no doubt that my father's equipage would be a most handsome one for the rest of his life. Especially as he, since the day he saw his first automobile, had been firm in the belief that woman's place was next to the driver. Never behind the wheel.

Sad to relate, father did not have the opportunity to go for very many decorative drives with my mother. From the very moment they were married, for better or for worse, with car and with hearth, their family life seems to have unswervingly adhered to the ruthless laws of the multiplication table.

They never succeeded in keeping the members of

the family at a countable minimum. Whenever my father wanted to go for a drive with my mother, who still had green eyes, fair hair, and good looks, there was always a host of people who wished to go along. There was my father's younger brother Hugo, who had decided to honor our house with his presence for the duration of his studies. There was my mother's elder sister Agate, who came, by chance, to visit us at Easter, and who, in a moment of abnegation, took upon herself to fry the chickens. She did not have green eyes and her hair might more correctly be termed "week-day colored," but she was far better than my mother at frying chickens. That was why my father, after a short consultation with my mother, decided that she might as well remain, now that she was there anyway. My father felt that she must also be in possession of exceptional qualities as far as the preparation of yellow pea soup and brown cabbage and pork were concerned. This happily proved to be the case, thus assuring my aunt's future. Add to this the fact that my mother began to produce children and did not seem to be able to say "when." During the space of four years she added three children to the ménage: first me, then my sister, and then my brother. Our arrival completely changed the vision of elegant drives in green and brass which my father had seen as he stood at the altar with my mother.

Reality was as follows: My father's place was still behind the wheel in the little, green car. Next to him my mother. In front of her he placed my aunt Agate on a kitchen stool, and my little brother on her lap. At the back, in the dicky, my uncle Hugo sat in the middle and my sister and myself on each side of him. As we grew up my Uncle Hugo got more and more squeezed and I think this was the main reason for his making an effort to finish his studies so that he could get a car of his own.

Before things got to this stage, however, circumstances had obliged my father to replace his dream-car with another, the direct and immediate reason being the arrival of Thor.

Thor, for a change, was not an infant. He was a puppy and he arrived in our town with the soldiers during the Fall manoeuvres. Six infantry privates entered my father's shop desiring to exchange the dog for a box of cigars. They swore by the colors and their uniform that Thor was a Dalmatian. My father went upstairs to the flat and opened the encyclopaedia at D and learned that a Dalmatian would grow up to be about the size of a poodle. There was also a very pretty picture of a Dalmatian in the encyclopaedia. He took council with my mother; together they measured the car and decided that Thor would be able to sit up between them. So the soldiers got a box of cigars and we got a dog.

During the first Summer things went quite well, even though Thor preferred to lie down while we were driving. He placed his head in my mother's lap

and his stern in father's ditto. After my father had twice firmly seized his tail instead of the brake Thor learned not to wag it while the car was in motion. As Autumn drew on we couldn't help noticing that Thor was beginning to take up more and more space. It was becoming increasingly difficult to turn the wheel when he was present. The front part of him grew at such a rate as soon to hide from view the little that was still visible of my mother when both Aunt Agate and my brother were seated on the kitchen stool in front of her. Finally Thor, when in a recumbent position, reached from door to door. Once more father consulted the encyclopaedia. Once again he opened it at the letter D, but this time at DANE (GREAT), while we children looked over his shoulder. "Oh, look!" cried my sister and I, "There's a picture of Thor in the encyclopaedia!"

Anybody who possesses an encyclopaedia knows what it says about Great Danes. With funereal voice father read out that these faithful friends of man can go on growing until they are two years old and that they can become larger than a calf.

The next day my father sent for catalogues of new cars. In his letter he stressed the fact that he needed a large car.

This time my father chose an open Chevrolet. A very large, blue, open Chevrolet. According to our calculations there should now be a seat for everybody, even Thor.

The same morning that the car arrived and collected a throng of curious in the street outside, because nobody in our town had yet seen a car of such dimensions, a letter arrived from my grandparents in Jutland. Mother read it aloud while father stood at the window contemplating his new car. As she worked her way through the missive his expression, which had been one of marked enthusiasm, gradually changed to one of deep thoughtfulness. The letter related that mother's parents had a big and delightful surprise in store for us. My grandfather was being pensioned off that coming summer and had decided to move to Zealand. He had arranged that he and granny should go and live at Gimmersoe, only a few miles from their dear children. They were both looking forward very much to participating in our Sunday excursions. In a postscript my grandfather announced that mother's younger sister, Feodora, had become engaged to a student of arboriculture, and at her instigation grandfather had decided to settle within the arboriculturist's sphere of action. He, too, was looking forward to taking part in the family motoring excursions, of which he had heard so much.

This letter resulted in my mother's first request that she should be allowed to learn to drive the car. She described to my father how she would be able to take out her aging parents, not to mention her sister Feodora and her aboriculturist.

My mother, who hitherto had been quite content

to see her parents at Christmas and during the summer holidays only, worked up a mother-and-father fixation during the weeks that followed the arrival of the Chevrolet and the letter, and this was mobilized in attacks of increasing intensity against my father. She also used other methods, amongst them the approximation of her appearance and behavior to that of Miss Mary Pickford. During this period she talked baby-talk to such an extent that even my five-year old brother was an elderly gentleman compared to her. As my father continued adamant she adopted still other methods. For a whole month she was Pola Negri, a dangerous woman with a fringe, a very small mouth and audacious garters.

My father pretended not to notice. He stood fast on his sole right to the wheel of the Chevrolet and to being in charge of its abundant contents on the roads of the island of Zealand. Having successfully withstood all attacks during a period of two months, he was so sure of his victory that he ventured to boast of it to his friends.

This was the moment when my mother launched her decisive attack. She became a suffragette.

Things would not have come to this pass if my mother hadn't met our gymnastics teacher, Miss Liljekvist-Sorensen, at a parents' meeting at the local girls' school, which my sister and I attended. Up to that day mother had scarcely been aware that there was such a thing as a suffragette movement, never so far having felt the need of one. Up to this point in her existence she had been of the opinion that men were a most excellent invention. Even my father's opposition to her wish to seize the wheel would scarcely have influenced her point of view if Miss Liljekvist-Sorensen had not marched into her life. What she told my mother about men over the coffee and cakes after the parents' meeting will never be revealed, but her confidences were undoubtedly based indirectly on one wrecked engagement and an unrequited passion for the vicar, who took the Fourth in Latin.

At any rate mother came home and declared that we were living in a community full of domineering males and defenseless women. She whispered to my Aunt Agate of Miss Liljekvist-Sorensen's admirable steadfastness in opposing the male sex. If there were more women like Miss Liljekvist-Sorensen the world would be a very different place—women who kept their path clean, she added, and looked with vexation at my brother, my sister and me, the palpable proof that she herself, unfortunately, had not been able to say *no* in time. Aunt Agate comforted my mother by telling her that Miss Liljekvist-Sorensen had found it easier than my mother to keep her path clean; for Providence had provided my mother's new friend with protruding upper front teeth, a pointed nose that was always reddest where it was most pointed, dandruff, and a figure that looked as though she, at an early point in her life, had been seized by the top and shaken in such a manner as to cause the bulk of her insides to settle rather far down. Add to this the fact that she walked like a colonel in the Life Guards and that she had more than the suggestion of a mustache.

Miss Liljekvist-Sorensen began to call on us at home. When father was present she proved how well she was able to hide her aversion for the male sex, smiling horribly at him and laughing loudly at his jokes, which at that period of his life were becoming infrequent and unfunny. Never before or since have I seen such quantities of teeth at one time as when Miss Liljekvist-Sorensen was amused at something my father had said.

My sister and I, who only knew Miss Liljekvist-Sorensen from the school gym, discovered new sides to her character. Considering that eighty per cent of the black and blue marks my sister and I had on our collective bodies during our whole life were caused by Miss Liljekvist-Sorensen's sharp nails, it was a new and interesting experience to hear her calling us her little lambs and telling us in a smarmy voice that when we became grown up woman's fight would luckily be over and done with, and then it would be we and not our brother who would rule the world.

My sister said afterwards that she didn't care who ruled the world so long as it wasn't Miss Liljekvist-Sorensen. This utterance cause my mother to lay hands on her.

Next day my sister and brother were lurking on the first floor, awaiting Miss Liljekvist-Sorensen's arrival. They had searched the nursery for things throwable and had finally decided to sacrifice my brother's rocking-horse, Musse. When Miss Liljekvist-Sorensen's firm footsteps were heard in the porch Musse was pushed onto the windsowsill. At the exact moment that she passed below Musse fell from the window accompanied by my brother's good wishes. Musse succeeded in hitting Miss Liljekvist-Sorensen's right hand only, thus for weeks reducing her to pinching her pupils with her left hand only. The rocking-horse was so much damaged that my uncle Hugo had to break off his studies for a whole week in order to put it together again.

In this case, too, Miss Liljekvist-Sorensen proved the strongest. Father undertook personally to punish my brother and sister. While mother and Miss Liljekvist-Sorensen talked heatedly in the drawing-room father went in to the children and promised them a penny each if they would howl for ten minutes. While their wild screams sounded through the house my father sat squashed into a child's chair looking very tired. Even though we were not very big and did not understand all that was going on, we sensed that he soon would be a beaten man, and that the time was not far off when mother would be sitting behind the wheel in his blue Chevrolet.

The war entered its last phase on the afternoon

that Miss Liljekvist-Sorensen and mother in vain attempted to persuade Aunt Agate to become a suffragette. When my aunt, who was in charge of the housekeeping, declared that she didn't have time for such stuff, Miss Liljekvist-Sorensen undoubtedly realised that this would prevent her from launching the decisive attack. So long as a man is fed and so long as there is some semblance of order around him, it is amazing what he will put up with. The final thrust would have to come from another quarter.

Next morning Miss Liljekvist-Sorensen and my mother went off to Copenhagen together. When they returned my mother was wearing a reform dress. The appearance of this ghastly article of apparel in our otherwise presentable home decided the matter. My little brother burst into tears. The nursemaid informed my Aunt Agate that she was considering giving notice. Father wanted no dinner that evening; he and mother had a long talk alone in the study.

We children never saw mother wearing the reform dress again. Next morning my mother appeared in one of her dresses from the Mary Pickford period. She told us that she had good news for us all. She was going to learn to drive the car.

The local driving instructor was an elderly man whose name was Mogensen. He came and fetched mother in his own car for her first lesson and they didn't come back for three hours. It turned out that my mother had driven into a heap of stones at the edge of the road, puncturing two tires in the process. My father later in life used to say that Mogensen returned from that drive an older man. Next day Mogensen didn't come himself. Instead he sent his son. This was a handsome, sunburned young man who seemed glad to be alive. So handsome and so glad, indeed, that my father suggested that mother should invite Miss Liljekvist-Sorensen along. Mother did not think this was a good idea. Father then suggested that Thor should sit in the back of the car. I don't know what father had in mind.

Thor went along three times, after which the driving instructor insisted that the dog should remain behind. Mother couldn't see to back up the car with Thor sitting high and mighty on the back seat; he pointed accusingly at a scratch on the rear near fender. My father asked both maids and Aunt Agate whether they would like to go for a nice drive, but they all backed out. Finally he asked mother if she didn't think it a good idea if she wore her reform dress on these trips, seeing that she had it anyway?

Mother did not think so. Anyway she was beginning to be bored with the driving lessons. She knew it all now. With a dazzling smile she asked young Mogensen if he didn't think she was ready to pass the test soon, and since he appears to have had a higher regard for his car than for mother's company, he declared that she would be ready after a few more lessons.

"By all means," said my father hopefully, "let her try as soon as possible."

Later in life I have heard many harsh words about the heartless members of the body of motor-vehicle examiners. There are the stories of examiners who neither greet you on arriving nor take leave upon departing. There are the harrowing accounts of examiners who expect of the candidate for a driving license, whose nerves are already in a state of turmoil, almost professorial motoring erudition as to the finer points of the hidden, technical world beneath the hood of the car.

My mother's examiner, old Mr. Andersen, was not like that. He personally came and fetched her, politely opened the door of the car for her, and doffed his hat to the assembled family. He was an elderly man and my mother had met him socially at dinner parties; she had been in some suspense, wondering whether it would be old Andersen or his colleague Lieutenant Skrappenborg who would have the pleasure of examining her. It was common knowledge that there was no relationship between what these two men expected their candidates to know. While old Andersen, whom my mother had drawn in the driving-test lottery, was a kindly man with solid roots in local society, whose last wish would have been to lay himself out with one of the town's better families by failing one of its members, Lieutenant Skrappenborg was a man of quite another caliber. He it was who had once asked

the bank manager to tell him about the proper adjust-
ment of the headlamps, and then refused him a driving
license because he knew nothing whatsoever about
the subject. The story was three years old and the
bank manager had subsequently obtained a license
during his summer holidays on the east coast of Jutland. But our town still referred to Lieutenant Skrappenborg as a man without veneration for his fellow
citizens, a hard man who didn't care which side his
bread was buttered on. Possibly this was because he
was from the town of Lemvig, whose natives are
known throughout Denmark as being faithful fol-
lowers of the rule-book.

Most candidates read up on the rules of the road
just to be on the safe side, in case they should draw
Skrappenborg for their test. My mother had no time
to do this. For one thing the weather was much too
fine, or at least so she said, and for another she considered that she was quite capable of driving a motor-
vehicle without knowing in detail how the brake
functioned, so long as it worked, and the least my
father could do was to see that it did.

My father's last hope disappeared when he saw that
old Andersen and not Skrappenborg waited for my
mother that summer morning when she was to pass
the final test. Old Andersen gallantly invited Thor to
sit on the back seat, so mother said that in that case
he would have to look out for anything coming up
behind them. Thor sat next to the driving instructor

on the back seat. They made almost as handsome a couple as my mother and old Andersen in front. We children cheered as mother stepped on the gas and made the car execute a series of coquettish little hops, skips and jumps, as it started on its way along the road.

Old Andersen had little in common with other motor-vehicle examiners. At least I don't think they usually come back and have coffee afterwards. But an hour later we heard mother clucking and cackling on the stairs, and when my father opened the door and saw old Andersen with a bag of cakes in his hand, he realized that all was lost. My mother had passed the test and obtained her driving license.

"By the way, Harald," mother said to father during the animated coffee-party afterwards, "you'll have to pop down to Ostergade number seven—or is it nine?—anyway it's a place where they have chickens. You're to pay for two . . ."

"Two what?" my father asked.

"Two chickens, of course," my mother replied.

"What chickens? Are we having them for dinner?" asked my father.

"No," my mother said, with a slight touch of irritation. "They are chickens that got under the car while I was driving."

"It was not your wife's fault altogether," old Andersen said and took another cake.

"Two chickens," my father repeated. "I have heard

of motorists running over one chicken by mistake, but two at a time . . ."

We could see that he was staring into a dark and threatening future.

During the days that followed father proved that he still had strength left to enable him to refuse to lend mother the big blue car. I have no doubt that this was why Miss Liljekvist-Sorensen was called up again. During a whole week she sat and bared her teeth at father's weak jokes, while at the same time, by interspersing judicious comments, she endeavored to maintain mother on her road to complete emancipation. Twice mother ostentatiously removed the reform dress from its moth-proof container and brushed it.

This proved too much for poor father's nerves. This must have been the time when he made up his mind to write off his car and instead concentrate on plans for the extermination of Miss Liljekvist-Sorensen and all that she stood for. One evening my mother attended a suffragette meeting with her friend and addressed the audience, as was faithfully reported in the local papers. Father decided on new tactics.

At the breakfast-table he ingratiatingly inquired if mother would care to take Miss Liljekvist-Sorensen for a drive in the car.

"A nice, long drive, Dagmar!" he added.

My sister and I were that day the most popular girls in school, as word spread like a forest fire from the first to the sixth grade, that Miss Liljekvist-Sorensen was going on a dangerous expedition that very afternoon. Perhaps we would never see her again. Perhaps, thanks to our mother, we should have a new teacher of gymnastics. Perhaps—and this I am afraid is where our wishes ran amok into a vision of Utopia—perhaps this new teacher would be a normal human being, who was married and had small children of her own and knew how such delicate creatures should be treated.

On our way home from school my sister and I thought out all the motoring accidents by which a car could be cut through lengthways, leaving the driver unscathed while at the same time grinding the passenger to a fine powder. We even went so far as to imagine Miss Liljekvist-Sorensen's interment. The flag at half-mast over the school, the principal addressing us in a shaking voice, and the choir of relieved children's voices.

We arrived home in time to witness the departure. It was on this occasion that our good dog Thor showed the high degree of his intelligence. He flatly refused to enter the car, even though mother coaxed with doggy talk and Miss Liljekvist-Sorensen hung over the other door, coaxing with all her teeth in the open air.

As evening fell a gay tooting was heard from the road. There was mother in the Chevrolet, both she, the car, and Miss Liljekvist-Sorensen, appeared to be in the best of health. As she swung into the garage a moment later she ran over my Uncle Hugo's bicycle, but nobody took much notice of this in the heat of the excitement at mother's return, a mixture of relief that both she and the car had reached safe port, and disappointment that Miss Liljekvist-Sorensen was still with us.

Like Noah who sent out the dove several times running to see if the earth was habitable, father now sent out Miss Liljekvist-Sorensen as my mother's trial passenger, to see if one might entrust more precious cargoes to her motoring care. He had given up hope of seeing my mother's mustachioed lady friend as the victim of a major mishap. He now simply hoped that mother would gradually become just as tired of seeing and hearing her as the rest of us were.

As far as I recall, nothing exciting happened on these trips, apart from the day when mother came home and asked if we didn't think it would be nice to have roast suckling pig for dinner. As the thought did not appeal to either Aunt Agate or father, mother began to praise this dish so much that a terrible suspicion entered my father's mind.

"You'd better confess straight out, Dagmar!" he said and looked mother fixedly in the eye.

"The little body is under that bit of tarpaulin in the back of the car," mother informed him. "It happened when we drove into a farmyard to turn around. I don't much care for backing and you have no idea how suddenly a pig like that can come running. Miss

Liljekvist-Sorensen advanced the money, so will you please give her fifty kroners. The farmer said it was a very fine pig."

While my father mumbled mother talked soothingly to him, saying that it might have been much worse. It might have been the farmer himself or his dog. Neither farmers nor their dogs are edible, and the pig was. And now we could have a dinner party and Miss Liljekvist-Sorensen should be guest of honor.

This innocent little pig, my mother's victim, was to be the indirect cause of Miss Liljekvist-Sorensen definitely leaving our home never to return. In future only my sister and I had the pleasure of her company at school. For at the aforementioned dinner party she became inebriated to such an extent that she bodily attacked my Uncle Hugo. All her principles in so far as men were concerned evaporated in a haze of alcohol. Mustache quivering, she hacked her prominent front teeth firmly into my Uncle Hugo's left ear-lobe. It came as a dreadful surprise to mother that her one-time friend hid such sinful and unsuffragette-like lusts in her flat bosom. After the party, having soothed terrified Uncle Hugo, she declared that her home was no Sodom, and that she was writing off the suffragette movement forever.

The reform dress was made into trousers for my brother.

The sense of peace and tolerance that now descended on our happy home resulted directly in a spontaneous promise from father that mother should one day be allowed to take the assembled family for a drive. Mother insisted that her aged parents, her sister Feodora, and the arboriculturist, should be of the party, and so one lovely Sunday morning in early fall father took place at the wheel of the big blue car. Next to him sat mother, in front of her Thor, in the back Aunt Agate, Uncle Hugo, my sister and I, and on a stool at our feet my little brother.

At Gimmersoe, where my grandfather was enjoying the evening of his life, we shifted our load. My Aunt Agate was once more placed upon a kitchen stool in front of my mother with my little brother on her lap. Thor sat between my father and my mother. In the back was my Uncle Hugo, grandfather and grandmother, and the arboriculturist with my Aunt Feodora on his lap. In front of them, precariously perched, each with one half of our respective posteriors on my brother's stool, sat my sister and I, counting the audible smacks that resounded every time the arboriculturist kissed my Aunt Feodora.

My father set course for a large and uninhabited forest. On a wide road, right in the middle, he stopped the car, looked all around, listened carefully to see if any living creature was stirring, changed places with my mother, and pronounced the magic words:

"Now you, Dagmar!"

Mother carefully moved the gear-lever. Into reverse, as it turned out. And thus it was that the big blue car, with father and mother, our good dog Thor, my grandfather, my grandmother, my Aunt Agate, my Aunt Feodora and her arboriculturist, (whose name, by the way, was Egon) my Uncle Hugo, my sister, my brother and I, moved majestically backwards into the ditch.

It took my mother and father, grandfather, grandmother, Uncle Hugo, Aunt Agate, Aunt Feodora, the arboriculturist, my sister, my brother and myself, a whole afternoon to get the car back on *terra firma*.

My mother never drove a car again. The subject was not touched upon in our home, and my father became known as a man of unswerving principles as far as women and car-driving was concerned. He was respectfully listened to when this subject was discussed among men.

That Sunday afternoon in the forest near Gimmersoe, so many years ago, when his big blue Chevrolet was firmly fixed with its rear end in the ditch, my father swore that neither his wife, his daughters, nor indeed any other woman, should ever obtain a driving license if he could help it.

chapter 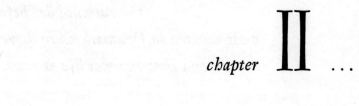 ...

*. . . which is about how my sister met
the automobile, before
most women in Denmark were drivers,
and how she met life as a result.*

When my father decided that only men should drive into the age of the combustible engine and that women should keep in the background—that they, at the very most, should sit beside men—he didn't dream that a time would come when bylaws and the penal code would necessitate the presence of wives behind the wheel of the family car.

When my father started to drive there was almost a whole road for every motorist. You had the road to yourself. The only obstacles to circumvent were dogs taking their midday ease in the roadway, and children playing hopscotch.

No policeman ever dreamed of asking whether the driver of a motor-vehicle was in possession of the requisite qualifications for navigating the highways. Nobody was interested in the percentage of alcohol in the driver's bloodstream.

True, it was considered a breach of the law, even then, to run over old women and children, but it was not until traffic became general that the authorities saw fit to meddle in the motorist's driving life.

Husbands could zig-zag home through deserted streets in peace, when returning from business meetings, lodge meetings, and other meetings. They felt no latent need for driving licenses for wives.

Whether the wives felt any latent need—and whether they were able to get it filled—depended on the individual husband's authority—or lack of same— within the family circle.

In those days, when a woman was seen driving her husband's car, all the other husbands knew how things stood in that family. A wife behind the driving wheel with her husband beside her was the outward and visible sign that Mother wore the pants.

In exactly the same way that a wife behind the wheel today may be the outward and visible sign that Father beside her is wearing the red red nose.

But other times were on the way.

When a sufficient number of inebriated cheerleaders and diners-outers and consumers of liquid business lunches had knocked down a sufficient number of more or less blameless pedestrians and cyclists, the authorities began to take an interest in the sobriety of motorists. And as more and more men knew somebody who had been "hauled in" as a consequence of driving humidly, they began to consider whether it would not be practical if the little woman learned to drive.

As time went by firm principles tottered in many families. More and more women were seen behind more and more wheels.

But in our home things were as they always had been. Our father preferred to take the opposite, and bitter, way. He refrained from imbibing if he was intending to drive home. No offering was great enough to lay on the altar of his principles.

My sister and I thus were quite grown up and had long ago left school before we were allowed to even approach the front seat of our successive family automobiles.

Our young brother, on the other hand, had been allowed to try his hand at driving from earliest childhood. Whenever we found ourselves on some lonely stretch of road my father would allow him to take the wheel and thereby fill the collective family—with the sole exception of my father—with horror equal to that which we had felt on that fateful afternoon when my mother drove a car for the last time.

Having always been a quiet and uncomplaining child, I unquestioningly accepted this state of things. My sister, an imaginative and gifted girl, who was taking political science at the University, was determined to mutiny in one way or another. She was not sure how until she happened to get hold of a revolutionary Russian novel.

In this she read that the women in the new Russia were allowed not only to sweep the streets and grease machines on an equal footing with men, but that they were found worthy to drive both trucks and tractors. It didn't mention private cars, but that was immaterial. From that moment my sister entered her communistic phase.

She first of all gave expression to her emancipation by donning a costume beside which my mother's re-form dress had been a piece of feminine coquetry.

She wore large flat shoes with rubber soles, cotton stockings of reddish hue and indescribably awful texture, a pleated skirt that did not reach the knees, and a reefer coat that, when buttoned, covered all but six inches of the skirt. Over one shoulder she slung a bag which it took her only one week to give the desired greasy and tattered appearance. Her lightly waved hair she cut short and curry-combed down flat over the ears, where it was kept in place with two conspicuous clips.

Her exterior thus in order, she began to invite fellow communists home. They looked exactly like her, apart from the fact that the males all had pimples and wore glasses and were perpetually hungry.

While they consumed Aunt Agate's roasts and emptied father's bottles they sometimes discussed how my father's business might best be shared out, and how our home could be divided into lots and become the

dwelling place of many happy right-thinking, or—to put it more precisely—left-thinking families.

But mostly they discussed the finer things of life, such as how to convert all the members of the Conservative People's Party before it was too late.

My father was such a member and I regret to have to say that he pigheadedly refused to be changed. On the contrary, it was as if he became daily more conservative under the influence of my sister's comrades.

He had never been so conservative as that evening —in the middle of an election—when my sister came home and proudly announced that she had hit a member of the Young Conservatives over the head with a rubber truncheon.

As a consequence of this my father agreed to pay my sister a fixed monthly sum so that she could leave home and go and live in a boarding house in Copenhagen. She could then sit with her comrades, my father said, and share anything she wished. And if in the future she felt a craving to take part in fighting, would she have the goodness to keep her hands off his customers' children—whatever political party they belonged to.

Of my sister's boarding house period very little is known. We only know that she returned home after two months with an entirely new coif, with entirely new political beliefs—and an enormous amount of unwashed linen.

She had become engaged to marry a perfectly

ordinary young man who had no desire to share out my father's estate among his friends and no ambition to change my father's political color. But he did think, on the other hand, that his wife-to-be should possess the necessary qualifications of a good housewife.

As soon as my Aunt Agate heard him say this— and fearful that this paragon of the male sex should disappear—she ran to my sister's room and locked the door. My sister's room always looked as if it had just been struck by a bomb.

At the same time my sister announced to her flabbergasted family that she intended to discontinue her university studies and take a position in a really classy home where she could learn housekeeping.

To emphasize her intention of going from one extreme to another, she read aloud in her new, soft, feminine voice, an advertisement she planned to answer. It read—in all its moving simplicity—as follows:

> *Young undergraduate of good family may obtain post as domestic-science pupil. Must be willing to help two sweet boys with lessons.*
> Apply to: Baroness Lulli von Loevenkopf, at "Mulevadgaard."

"You can't beat the Danish nobility for class," said my sister.

My sister got the job and it was arranged that she should take up her duties on the first of the following month.

When she returned after her interview with the Baroness Lulli von Loevenkopf she was very thoughtful and subdued, and we all thought that her meeting a lady of such exalted rank had maybe been too much for her.

To our relief she explained that the Baroness' maiden name had been Olsen, but that she was a woman of substance, her father having made an enormous fortune through the exploitation of cow-dung. Herr Olsen had, it seemed, invented a process whereby it was dried, ground to a powder, and exported as manure.

Old man Olsen had died long ago, but cows' digestions continued unabated, and his factories were still grinding and exporting at full speed. Every time a shipload of processed cow-droppings left a Danish port, money poured into his daughter's country estate of Mulevadgaard. The Baroness made no secret of the fact that the Baron—who was sixty and suffered from palsy—could thank old man Olsen for being still domiciled in the lovely surroundings of the ancestral home.

As the Baroness once expressed it: "If it weren't for me Carl-Johan would still be selling woodshavings and dirty rags!"

My sister had only caught a passing glimpse of the

two sweet boys. They were busy shooting with an air-gun at the cook's underwear which had been hung up to dry on the clothesline. Their mother had explained to my sister that they were such fun-loving, imaginative children.

Everything thus seemed to indicate that my sister might look forward to spending an interesting time with the nobility. But suddenly, in the middle of dinner, just as we all thought her immediate future well and happily mapped out, she burst into tears, struck her breast in a *mea culpa* manner, and cried: "I'm a swindler!"

"But my dear Agnete," my mother said, "whatever do you mean?"

My father paled. There had never been any swindlers in his family—apart from his uncle who cheated at pinochle.

Agnete soon composed herself and explained that her desire to work for the aristocracy had caused her to utter a falsehood.

The Baroness had first of all asked her if she could exercise a couple of the horses from the Mulevadgaard racing stables, to which she had readily replied that she could. True, she had never exercised a race horse before, but as far as she knew no special experience was required to ride race horses.

Further to this she was to give the housekeeper a helping hand, keep her own and the boys' rooms, help them with their lessons, lay the breakfast table, massage the Baroness' back and walk the two dachshunds. And last but not least. . . .

And here Agnete burst into tears again.

It was some time before we learned what was last but not least. At last we gathered that on top of all her other duties Agnete also had to drive the two sweet boys to school in the nearest town every day.

My father interpolated that as they seemed to have plenty of horses this should present no problem.

"But it's an automobile!" my sister cried, "and I told her I had a driver's license!"

To this day I don't know whether it was all a trick. If it was it was pretty smart.

Faced with the necessity of having to choose between foregoing his principles and risking family dishonor, my father finally gave in. The poor man didn't have much time in which to consider. I think that it was only the fact that Agnete would be practicing on another man's car that made his defeat bearable.

For the second time a woman of our family went to Mogensen's School of Driving.

Young Mogensen's efforts to teach a long line of pupils the rudiments of driving in the shortest possible time had aged him considerably.

Agnete began negotiations by announcing that she would only have time for six lessons before leaving to take up her exalted duties. On the other hand, it must definitely be admitted that she read up on the rules of the road most diligently. The theoretical side of driving has always been her strong point.

We all stood assembled and spat and crossed thumbs for her on the morning that she went up for the test. Her examiner was to be Lieutenant Skrappenborg who was unfortunately still going strong. Not so old Andersen. He had given up the ghost a couple of years before as a consequence of the shock he received when a candidate backed the car square into the window of a provision dealer. Old Andersen had managed to grant the pupil her license before turning blue in the face and being taken off to a hospital. That was old Andersen's last time out, a fact that my sister Agnete much regretted.

"If only nothing gets in my way I shall be all right," my sister said. "But cyclists and pedestrians make me nervous."

The sun shone from a clear sky and the traffic was lively and bustling while Agnete and her driving instructor stood and waited for the lieutenant to turn up.

Skrappenborg came slowly out of the Police Motor Office, and at the same instant it was as though an evil spirit flew across the heavens. Black clouds quickly piled up. There came a deafening clap of thunder and the rain began to pour down, obliging Lieutenant Skrappenborg to throw dignity to the winds and run the last ten yards to the car.

My sister drove through the flood at twenty miles

an hour in a town that was suddenly devoid of inhabitants, while explaining to Lieutenant Skrappenborg that one should always drive slowly on wet roads. He nodded his head approvingly and asked my sister to turn the car around. While she was backing it there was a tremendous crack of thunder that completely blotted out the sounds of my sister running over a parked bicycle. It fell over without the lieutenant's noticing anything, and my sister drove back in triumph to the Motor Office where she passed the theoretical test with flying colors.

At the luncheon table my sister's driving license was passed from hand to hand. We realized that it was almost a historical document. When it reached my father he looked as if he would most of all like to burn it. Instead he went into his office and wrote a check for Mogensen in compensation for the scratch caused by my sister's torpedoing the bicycle.

We had expected that my sister's stay in such exalted circles would set its stamp on her. This was not the case however. At least not in the way we had expected. This was because all the time she worked for the Baroness Lulli von Loevenkopf she had such trouble with fleas.

Apart from her numerous other duties in that distinguished house she had to share her bed with the two long-haired dachshunds, who were chronically infected with fleas. The baroness explained her wish that the dogs should sleep in Agnete's bed by telling her that they had shared the bed of my sister's predecessor and were used to sleeping there.

On top of the flea business, the fact emerged that the Mulevadgaard automobile was like no other automobile in Agnete's experience. It was the first gearless car in Denmark, a gigantic American crate of a vehicle that had formed part of some goods received in exchange for powdered cow-dung.

All that my sister had learned from Mogensen, and all that she had picked up by watching my father handle his various cars was wasted. She wrote and told us that the only experience that was of any use to her was what she had learned from time to time when using my mother's electric sewing machine which was equipped with a foot-pedal.

Tormented by flea bites and completely ignorant of what went on under the hood of the car, Agnete set off every morning for the town fifteen miles from Mulevadgaard. Her passengers were the two sweet boys who every day, by one means or another, retarded the time of departure, thus forcing my sister to drive at top speed.

As soon as they were all on their way the boys rolled down the windows and kept a sharp lookout for unsuspecting pedestrians on the idyllic country roads. Just before Agnete overtook someone the two sweet little barons would yell out such words as *bastard* or *son of a bitch* in high girlish voices, and then throw themselves down on the floor of the car.

My sister would go sailing by, red of face, and apparently alone in the car. It soon became known all over the countryside that the baroness' new servant not only drove like a madwoman at top speed, but that she was also a most improper person.

As the boys' vocabulary gradually expanded to include epithets even more pithy and unmentionable, the natives' suspicion of Agnete increased to such a degree that they also named her the author of all the obscene things that were written and drawn on the walls of the ladies' restroom at the railroad depot.

It will thus be readily understood that my sister was looking forward to the beginning of the summer vacation when she would no longer have to drive the fun-loving little boys to school.

But her anticipation was premature. The baroness had discovered my sister's prowess as a driver. She decided that Agnete was to be exempt from all other duties during the summer, so as to enable her to drive the baroness to her manifold errands in town.

The day of the Danish Derby was getting nearer and the baroness was personally engaged. Not to run herself, but as a focal point in the owners' enclosure.

Just as enormous sums were spent on sumptuous trappings for the horses and colors for the Mulevadgaard jockey, so Baroness Lulli von Loevenkopf was herself to be fitted out by her Copenhagen couturier, Herr Jarmerlund.

Herr Jarmerlund would have to hoist all sails and surpass himself once again, for while the readers of the morning papers naturally did not know which horses they would see depicted in the newspapers the day after the Derby, they did know that the reports would be copiously illustrated with photographs of the same three ladies they were used to seeing every year in the morning papers the day after the Derby. These were Fru Lissen Ubius, wife of the well-known manufacturer of tarpaulins and snowfences, Fru Pipsen Hagenbach, wife of the shipowner, and the Baroness Lulli von Loevenkopf of Mulevadgaard.

My sister thus took on a task of major importance when she agreed to convey the baroness between her home and Herr Jarmerlund's establishment in Copenhagen. Herr Jarmerlund was constantly on the verge of a nervous breakdown at the thought that his competitor, Monsieur Hugo, should succeed in surpassing him in the draping of Fru Lissen Ubius or Fru Pipsen Hagenbach.

My sister held his glass of sherry and his pincushion while he fastened pink organza to the baroness and told her of the reports he had received from the spies he had sent out. A sweet young man of whom he saw a good deal was a seamstress in Monsieur Hugo's establishment. He had stolen a bit of the stuff for Fru Pipsen Hagenbach's *création*. It was green with polka dots.

"My dear, I shudder at the very thought of seeing her with it on!" said Herr Jarmerlund. "With her complexion—the poor creature!"

And he hid his face in his hands and groaned while the baroness poured out their third glass of sherry and eagerly asked what Lissen Ubius was going to wear.

"My dear, you'll never guess! What *do* you think, Jensen, dear?" Herr Jarmerlund said to my sister, who in her capacity of chauffeur was now addressed by her surname. The baroness had made it clear that one couldn't have a chauffeur called Agnete.

"Tarpaulins and snowfences?" my sister guessed.

But Herr Jarmerlund was in no mood for facetiousness. He tossed off his glass of sherry and sent her a reproachful look, whereupon he announced in a voice of doom that Lissen Ubius, with the help of Monsieur Hugo, was going to commit the awful *faux-pas* of appearing in bright red—trimmed with monkey fur.

My sister made the acquaintance of many other chauffeurs who also waited outside while their masters and mistresses were being fitted by Herr Jarmerlund. They passed the time in a cellar café, and during these months my sister learned to play a mean game of billiards.

At the hour agreed upon she would lay down her cue, mount the steps to the street and go to meet the baroness, who had begun to retire more and more frequently to the Hotel d'Angleterre bar to refresh herself before undertaking the journey home.

These pauses for refreshment became more and more prolonged as the summer dragged itself out, and even an innocent girl like my sister could not help but notice that the baroness did not pause alone. With her was always a young man who in many respects was quite unlike the baron.

For one thing he was not a landed baron. He was "something" at one of the Latin embassies; for another he was not sixty, but around thirty-five; and finally he did not shake. On the contrary his hand was very steady as he pinched my sister's bottom while getting into the car one day to be driven to the next bar with the baroness.

And so it happened that my sister found herself more and more needed as private chauffeur. Instead of learning how to perform minor culinary miracles in the von Loevenkopf kitchens, she was now permanently ensconced behind the wheel of the von Loevenkopf automobile.

We saw nothing of her during these months, but friends and acquaintances who had been on visits to the Capital brought tales of how they had seen her waiting here and there with her car.

One had seen her outside the main entrance to Tivoli, another had seen her standing at attention at the door of the car as the baroness and her swarthy companion left it to enter the Wonder Bar.

Our Dean and his wife had even spoken to her once as she waited with the car one summer evening out-

side one of the parks. Agnete had confided to the
Dean's shocked wife that the baroness and her diplo-
matic escort had disappeared in the park an hour
before. She was now on the lookout for them among
the loving couples emerging from the bushes.

The good lady's account caused my mother to write
to Agnete and ask if she did not think that she could
learn housekeeping just as well at home.

"True," my mother wrote, "life isn't quite as event-
ful at home, but on the other hand," so it seemed to
my mother, my sister would be better able to concentrate on the work itself.

"There are other things in life," my mother added,
"than sitting at the wheel of a motor car."

We had not expected to see my sister before the
first of the following month. It therefore came as a
complete surprise to us all when Agnete returned one
lovely night in July with a wild look in her eyes. She
declared that she had run away from her job and that
she never again as long as she lived would work for
the landed nobility.

My father and mother asked her if she didn't think
she ought to tell the baron and baroness of her decision, but Agnete assured them that they were well
aware of it. Apart from this she was unwilling to explain how she had managed to get from Mulevad-

gaard's isolated homestead to the provincial town of her childhood.

It was not until the next morning that my sister asked me in a whisper whether I would like to get a glimpse of the baroness. Upon my asking how this could be accomplished, my sister led me from our house and along the main street. In front of the Town Hall all was peaceful. It was Sunday and that matinal hour when the last nightly revelers had gone home and the first early risers were not yet abroad.

In the market square a single automobile was parked. It was a very large automobile. It appeared to be deserted, but my sister made a sign that I was to stroll past it and cast a glance inside, while she waited behind one of the pillars of the Town Hall.

I did so and in the car I saw a lifeless body. Clammy from horror I thought that things had come to a pretty pass when my sister had murdered her mistress. I had no doubt that the ravaged blonde sprawled on the back seat must be the Baroness Lulli von Löevenkopf.

While I stood there motionless and imagined Agnete spending the next thirty or so years wasting away in a prison for women as a punishment for her untameable desire to drive automobiles, the body suddenly moved, and even through the tightly closed windows I could hear it moaning faintly.

I flew back to where my sister was hiding and asked her if the baroness was injured.

"She's dead drunk," Agnete replied in a matter-of-fact voice, as though such a thing were an everyday occurrence.

We gave a last glance at the body in the car and then we walked home through the awakening town, while she told me how it had come to pass that the baroness was parked in our local market square.

For a whole month my sister had been planning to run away on her weekly day off. But the baroness had cancelled all my sister's days off because she had constantly to go to Copenhagen to see Herr Jarmerlund and the swarthy gentleman from the Latin embassy.

To contemplate flight on an ordinary weekday was out of the question. There was only one daily bus and train connection linking Mulevadgaard with civilization, and that was in the middle of the day—at which hour my sister was occupied in driving the baroness about far from Mulevadgaard.

She had planned to secrete her belongings in the baggage compartment of the car and to steal away while it was parked outside one of the numerous places of amusement that the baroness and her friend visited. Yesterday they were to pick up the pink creation (with ruffles) from Herr Jarmerlund's elegant establishment, and after that my sister reckoned to have plenty of opportunities for flight.

But in this she had been mistaken. The baroness and her Latin friend had suddenly decided to take their illicit love-making out into the lovely rural environs of the city.

My sister drove them from one inn to another, the baroness becoming more and more coy and kittenish at each stop along the way. When around midnight my sister set the course for Copenhagen in order to drop the Latin lover at his home, the baroness was, to put it mildly, in an advanced state of inebriation.

Before the baroness' boy friend could be delivered outside his front door, the last train had gone. The baroness, in a state of death-like torpor, had no thought for the morrow and the Derby.

Agnete, who had had enough, resolutely set out for her childhood home.

She parked the car containing the unconscious baroness and the box in which was Herr Jarmerlund's pink creation (with ruffles), in front of the Town Hall, and dragged her suitcase home on foot.

As we mounted the stairs in our father's house Agnete confided to me that she was sick and tired of driving and of baronesses and fancy tailors and Latin lovers and of fleas and fun-loving little boys.

On Monday morning my mother opened the paper to look at the pictures of the Derby. There were photographs of Fru Lissen Ubius "wearing a charming red creation with a fringe of monkey-fur" and of Fru Pipsen Hagenbach "as chic as ever in green dotted silk."

"I should have thought they would have had a picture of Baroness Lulli von Loevenkopf too," my mother said. "They usually do. Wasn't she going to wear pink organza, Agnete?"

"With ruffles," said my sister.

No doubt tens of thousands of other readers wondered why not a single Copenhagen morning or evening paper had seen fit to give them the lowdown on what the Baroness Lulli von Loevenkopf had worn in the owners' enclosure on Derby Day that year.

Only one person was able to give complete information about all the comings and goings on that day of the Baroness Lulli von Loevenkopf.

This was Police Sergeant Jensen of our home town. Towards church-time several elderly ladies on their way to the Church of Our Lady excitedly drew his attention to the parked automobile containing a body.

Police Sergeant Jensen opened the door of the car, sniffed, and refused to believe his own nose, which reported a strong concentration of alcoholic fumes which to his mind were not at all in keeping with the luxurious and elegantly appointed vehicle. On the back seat a woman was either dead or sleeping.

He prodded this person tentatively, whereupon she waved an arm uncertainly in the air and mumbled, "Drive on, Jensen dear! Drive on!" and collapsed again.

After that Police Sergeant Jensen was no longer in doubt as to where his duty lay. He got behind the wheel and drove straight to police headquarters.

And so ended the episode of my sister Agnete and the motor vehicle. Needless to say, the whole affair gave my father a sort of grim satisfaction, which, much to his credit, he expressed only occasionally and, all things considered, with admirable constraint.

chapter 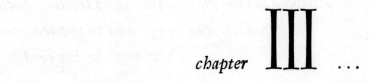 ...

*. . . which recounts how the road to
a driving license may go through a trotting-horse
(which may sound odd to the reader—
until he has read it).*

When other fathers marry off their daughters they whisper a "Be good to her" in the bridegroom's ear. Not so my father. Adamant in his principles as regards women and driving, he finished his speech to the man my heart had chosen with a "Never let her drive your car."

My new husband Peter nodded in complete agreement. He shared my father's opinion that a man should wear out his own car; that he is quite capable of doing that without help.

I bowed to my fate never to drive an automobile. I even got used to the idea. Being allowed to drive was a state of things quite outside the realm of the possible, and the sight of my friends one by one driving up to my house at the wheel of their husbands' cars sowed no seeds of discontent in my heart.

So long as there was air in the tires of my bicycle and the chain didn't rattle too loudly, and, later, so long as there was still room for baskets and extra clip-on seats for my growing flock of children, I didn't really mind.

Now and again when shopping with my two-year-old twins seated in front of the handlebars, my three-year-old son behind me, number four beside me, and our poodle stringing along attached to the handlebars, I would meet my husband driving our new Ford. He would wave to his collected family with a lordly gesture, and the children would wave back and the poodle would bark, while I would restrict myself to a careful nod out of consideration for the family equilibrium.

The year that the children numbered four, things took an unexpected turn. For one thing we were apparently in for a horrible summer. It rained continuously and the children were so noisy playing indoors that no man could be expected to stand it in his own house.

This was probably the reason why the father of my children came home one day with an expression on his face like the one his mother used to put on when she said brightly: "Today we're going to have some lovely hash for dinner."

"Guess what I've done today?" he said with a two-timing grin on his deceitful face. "I've rented a house for the summer for you and the children. You'll all be able to go and enjoy the sea and the summer weather."

I asked suspiciously where he was going to stay during that time. He replied that he was always prepared to sacrifice for his family. He was going to remain in the nasty old town and work to provide for all his hungry little mouths. He would visit us weekends to see how we were getting on. To prevent our being bored he and his friend Henry had decided that Henry's wife and two small children should come with us. There was plenty of room in the house, he said.

Room there was, and that's about all there was, as far as I could see. The house that Peter and Henry had chosen for Ellen and me and the children turned out to be as big as a convention hall. It was also in the same condition as a convention hall the morning after.

We arrived with our six collective children representing every degree of uncleanliness—and all ages from four down. The summer heavens let loose a downpour. We discovered immediately that there was a hole in the roof.

"What a wonderful time you're going to have living in such close touch with Nature," our menfolk said, while Ellen and I unpacked one hundred and thirty diapers and started wiping the first of the runny noses.

It was an unforgettable time. The storm howled and the sluicegates of heaven opened wide. The roof leaked and the children wet their pants and were hungry between mealtimes and refused to eat while there was food on the table.

Ellen and I became so proficient at washing and artificially drying diapers and pants that we would have been quite able to take in a medium-sized town's washing. We learned to dry diapers by the smoke method, which was practiced with the help of the only stove in the house. We invented the bed-drying method, which consisted of placing the diapers between layers of newspapers and putting these under Ellen and myself when we finally got to bed at night. Here, then, we "hatched" the children's clothes until the following morning, and this was interrupted only by frequent nightly visits to the nurseries when one or the other of the children screamed or was feverish or nearly died coughing.

No kind of cold is a stranger to me after that memorable summer. The children took turns at running temperatures of up to a hundred and three, and every time this happened Ellen and I took turns at jumping on a rusty old bicycle and pumping the five miles to the village doctor.

When he eventually turned up the child who had set off the alarm was usually back to normal again and screaming to go out and play. This was of no consequence however. A new case had always broken out in the meantime.

We got used to there always being something wrong. After we had lived this active life for three weeks, a Saturday dawned when it neither rained, hailed nor stormed; when none of the kids was sick and when the diapers seemed to dry by themselves in the open air.

We felt quite uneasy at this sudden and unexpected turn in the weather. In a state of slight incredulity we began, for the first time, to take some notice of our own appearance in anticipation of our husbands' imminent weekend visit.

As we washed and brushed and set our hair and lacquered our nails—a pastime we had not expected ever to be able to abandon ourselves to again—Ellen remarked that it was all too good to be true.

At that moment weird noises down by the picket fence portended new troubles. At the entrance to our damp paradise we found a man who asked us whether this would be Sunshine Drive number eight and said if it was he had a trotting-horse to deliver.

While I was discussing matters with the horse's messenger—who said that he expected my husband would explain everything when he turned up and that all we had to do in the meantime was to be kind to the horse—the five of our children who were able to crawl, totter or walk, crawled, tottered and walked in and out between the horse's legs. Ellen had to remove them by force before we led the animal into our yard and tethered it to a pine tree. It immediately began to consume all the sparse and wind-blown vegetation within reach.

We emptied one of the buckets containing dripping

diapers and filled it with water to drink, and the horse
seemed quite happy.

Two hours later Peter arrived. He came through
the gate with his usual gay remark about two women
having a wonderful time while their husbands were
slaving away in the city. I'm not sure that I was able
to echo his peaceful mood when I asked him how he
dared to inflict me not only with four children, but
with a trotting-horse as well?

Men think they have an infallible means of placating
irate wives. It consists of the simple little word "business."

Peter immediately took a firm hold of this old saw.
The horse, he said, was a link in a chain of business-
exchanges—a very complicated piece of barter indeed.
But if I would sit down and relax he would explain
everything.

He had taken possession of the horse in a suit
against a butcher. The man owed Peter fifteen hundred kroners, and that was a lot of money, my husband added, as if I didn't know it already. Peter had
had the choice between the horse and a harmonium,
these being part of a lot, the other parts of which
were the butcher's wife's dressing table and a picture
by an unknown artist. This last was an oil painting
of a woodland glade with an antlered deer.

My husband further explained in a superior tone of
voice that he had had the horse delivered to us in the
country because we could not house it in our apart-

ment in town. Here, on the other hand, he told us there was an excellent outhouse which, with a few alterations, could be converted into a temporary stable. Besides it was easier to sell a horse in the country than in the city. He had already inserted an advertisement in the local papers.

Thus it was that during the days that followed, the sun having finally been persuaded to shine, I had to give up participation in the gay, carefree life on the beach, and stay near the house to await possible buyers.

They came in droves, not only from the adjacent farms, but from the rural stores as well. I won't say that there weren't a few among them whose intention it was to buy the horse if they could get it for a couple of hundred kroners. But most of them only came to look at it and—it was my sad impression—to look at the fools in the summer house who had suddenly become the owners of a trotting-horse.

I took turns at walking around the horse with little, wizened men who had a sly, Home Mission kind of look in their eye; and big fellows with hearty, hail-fellow-well-met, Lutheran laughter on their lips.

Together we felt croup and fetlock, together we opened its mouth and counted *Liebergut's* teeth— Liebergut was the horse's name—together we pinched his skin and my paeans of praise wound themselves like verbal garlands around its brown flanks and its elegant mane, which Ellen brushed every morning, brushing all the childrens' hair being part of her daily chores anyway.

But it looked as though Liebergut was to remain with us forever in the temporary stable that Peter and Henry had made for it with the aid of forty kroners' worth of planks purchased from the local timber merchant. The merchant came to see the horse too, by the way, probably to see once more his wretched sticks and to laugh up his sleeve at having got forty kroners for them.

Every weekend Peter turned up and asked whether Liebergut had been sold and for how much. He was visibly disappointed not to be greeted by me with a couple of thousand kroners and no horse. Personally I was beginning to get used to the idea that Liebergut would be always with us. But Peter said that something would have to be done. Liebergut was a trotting-horse; he couldn't just stand there and eat oats all day. Peter was going to take the matter in hand and try to sell the horse himself.

In the middle of the week Peter drove up with a little, round man whose name was Enok.

He wanted to buy Liebergut but unfortunately he only had a hundred kroners at the moment. But the balance, fourteen hundred kroners, he would pay before the end of the week.

Once again we looked Liebergut in the mouth, smacked his croup and felt his fetlocks and pinched his hide, and Peter and Enok drank three bottles of beer, and then Enok said that that horse was fine and dandy.

We took fond leave of Enok, and the next day two men came and fetched Liebergut away. When Peter came back that weekend I asked him if he had received the fourteen hundred kroners from Enok. Peter said no, but Enok was all right.

"What does he do?" I asked, "apart from now being a horse-owner, I mean?"

"Enok is a driving instructor," Peter replied.

The following weekend there was a letter from Enok. Peter opened it expecting to find a check, I think. I got this impression from the way he examined the open envelope, holding it up to the light and frowning into it, before proceeding to read the letter.

Enok, it appeared was in momentary monetary difficulties. It might be some time before he could pay for Liebergut, but the day would come, he supposed, when Liebergut would win a race and then, naturally, he, Enok, would pay what he owed with interest on the interest. Further to this he had a suggestion to make. This was to the effect that we could take driving lessons for the money.

"I already know how to drive a goddam car!" Peter said.

After a further exchange of letters with Enok, Peter came out the following weekend and said in a depressed tone of voice that it would be another fourteen years before our son would be old enough to get a license.

"A pity all that money is lost. Perhaps we should take Liebergut back?" I suggested, and added that it was a shame that Enok had got the better of Peter.

Another two weeks went by before Peter got tired of waiting for his money. He came home that weekend a beaten man, and asked if I would care to learn to drive. As though to drag Henry with him in his fall, he added grandiosely that Ellen could learn to drive too.

The following Monday morning Enok rolled up in a Ford coupé of indeterminate age. In shape it reminded me of my father's first automobile. Like my father's first car this one had a hole in the back where from one to several persons could be stowed.

In this rumble seat we crammed as many children as possible, the whole flock in fact, with the exception of the baby who stayed at home with Ellen while I was driving, and with me when it was Ellen's turn.

We regarded these hours at home with only one child—and that the easiest child to keep an eye on— as pure bliss. This alone, so it seemed to us then, more than justified Enok's existence. I think none of us had yet properly realized the amazing fact that we were actually going to learn to drive a car.

Enok was a kindly man who possessed much of that pedagogical mildness of spirit which is supposed to have disappeared with the last of the old-fashioned school marms. Enok was apparently delighted no matter what you did to his car.

"Fine and dandy," he said when you made his gears crunch excruciatingly, and it was fine and dandy too, when you cut a corner going round a turn. It was even fine and dandy when I suddenly found myself sitting with the steering-wheel loose in my hand after having wrenched it around too hard. Not to mention how fine and dandy it was one day down in the Village when I backed the wrong way and draped the near hind fender lovingly and inextricably over a portion of the monument for the soldiers who fell at Dybbol in 1864.

All this was charged to Liebergut who, so Enok said, was *fine and dandy*.

For the children these trips were a great adventure, especially when we drew near to inhabited regions. Not far from our house there was a charming small provincial town, mentioned in tourist folders for its cobbled streets, its old houses, and the blessed peace that reigns in its quaint old streets. Enok chose this idyll when the time came for us to try and handle the car in something more complicated than the open country.

With mother at the wheel we rolled through the peaceful streets. Enok chose the midday hour when the town was even more lethargic than usual. But it is a known fact that small children can take only so much peace and quiet.

So Ellen's daughter Mette and my son Anders constructed an apparatus especially intended for these visits to the sleepy old town. It consisted of four tin cans on a string which they dragged after the car over the uneven cobblestones. This made such an infernal row that the townspeople rushed to their windows and pedestrians and cyclists fled across the sidewalk to press themselves up against the houses. Our daily entry into the town constituted a festive interruption of its humdrum existence. Our children enjoyed it too.

It must be said for Enok that he was very fond of children. When the five kids in the rumble-seat took to fighting and screaming, he was the mediator and conciliator who dragged a couple of them into the front seat with us and said they were fine and dandy children.

Even on the day when he was fined thirty kroners because the twins, Agnes and Benedicte, had held a broomstick at right angles from the back of the car, thus effectively obstructing overtaking traffic, Enok still said that all was fine and dandy.

"We'll charge it to Liebergut," he said, and added that he believed he only had the tail left to pay for, after which all of Liebergut would be his.

There only remained the driving test which unfortunately had to be taken in the Capital. So as to be on the safe side Enok reminded us that not all Police Examiners were fond of children. He suggested that we leave our issue behind when presenting ourselves for The Test.

Having put our names down for the test, Enok instituted inquiries so as to find out who our examiner was to be.

This was a matter of the utmost importance. According to Enok they all had their own favorite route. When he discovered that my examiner was to be a retired police-sergeant named Sorensen, he arranged a final lesson which was to ensure my victory.

He told me about Sorensen, about his manner, about his favorite theoretical subjects, about his gruff exterior which I was not to be impressed by, and about the route that Sorensen would tell me to take.

Accompanied by Enok, and for once with an empty rumble seat, I drove the car into Abel Katrinesgade (Abel Catherine's Street) one fine afternoon. Here we encountered six other learners' cars, all apparently manned by pupils expecting to be examined by Sorensen.

I practiced turning the car around, and as all the others were doing the same, we managed to stop all normal traffic in that street for more than a half hour.

Suddenly there appeared a car at the end of the street, at the sight of which we all scattered like chickens before the fox.

"Out of the way!" Enok yelled, and for once I couldn't drive fast enough to please him. It was the examiner, Sorensen himself, who had driven up with a victim.

Just as seafaring men have their unwritten laws,

so do driving instructors have theirs. One is to help a colleague and his pupil when taking the test.

With the drivers of three other learners' cars Enok and I effectively blocked off the street from other traffic until Sorensen was satisfied and ordered his examinee to return to the crowded streets of Copenhagen's West End.

After that we practiced backing until Enok said now would I tell him all about the braking system, for Sorensen was simply nuts about brakes.

When I was word-perfect at reeling off weird and completely uncomprehensible maxims about brakes and their linings and fittings and *raison d'être*, we passed on to the route itself.

Enok knew for sure that Sorensen would tell me to drive from Police Headquarters, through Stormgade (Storm Street) and up Bernstorffsgade (Count Bernstorff's Street). Then we would turn elegantly left past the Wivex restaurant and proceed through Vesterbrogade (West Bridge Street) ("And for heaven's sake watch out for tram Number 13, it's completely unpredictable!") After a number of sudden turns through minor side streets we would land in Abel Catherine's Street and turn right around in the manner prescribed by Enok. And after that everything would be absolutely fine and dandy, Enok added.

The next day Enok and I waited outside Police Headquarters.

"Wasn't Sorensen supposed to be here at eleven?"

I asked when it was a quarter past. I could see that Enok, for once, didn't think it was fine and dandy.

"For heaven's sake don't say 'Sorensen,' ma'am," he said. "Remember to address him by his title. In fact say as little as possible. Remember that though his manner may be gruff, he hides a heart of gold . . ."

At that moment the police inspector turned up.

In the town where I spent my childhood I often saw the mayor and the police inspector welcoming the King and the Queen and the Duke of Gloucester. It was very impressive. But those elegant bows and scrapes were as nothing compared to the way Enok greeted Police Inspector Sorensen.

First of all Enok flew out of the car and bowed twice without any response at all from the police inspector. For a moment I thought he had made a mistake and was bowing to a complete stranger. But Enok backed away on his fat little legs, and bowed and ducked and cackled and bowed again, and then the stranger actually mumbled something to him and got in next to me.

I gave him a dazzling smile and told him my name.

"Drive!" said the examiner, Police Inspector Sorensen. "Left. And now to the right . . ."

We were off.

I silently blessed Enok for having taken me over the course. Even at this early stage I sensed that The Grim Examiner at my side would not feel kindly disposed to the small handicap with which Nature had endowed me and which I had kept a secret up to that moment:

I am quite unable to make a snap decision as to which is right and which is left.

Before deciding which is which I have to go through a fairly complicated memory process. For example, if anybody asks me to turn to the left, I must first recall my childhood dancing lessons which took place in the Gobelin Room at the Posthorn Hotel.

At the far end of the great room I am standing and holding the hand of my dancing partner, Gustav, and we are four and five years old respectively.

The dancing teacher says, "Now we start off on our right foot, lifting it up high, and the right foot is the foot nearest to the wall."

My left foot must therefore have been the one farthest from the wall—and thus I know today which way to turn the car when someone says "turn left."

There are moments in life when it is not easy to return in a flash to the dancing school and Gustav and the wall in the Gobelin Room, as for example when you are attempting to pass the driving test with a silent and brooding police inspector at your side. That is why I am at this time especially fond of Enok. In a few moments we will be outside the Wivex restaurant where we turn left into West Bridge Street and make for Abel Catherine's Street.

"Right!" barks the Police Inspector.

I place myself correctly in the middle of the street, cast a glance over my shoulder and make sure that tram Number 13 is nowhere within sight, after which I turn left in one of the handsomest curving sweeps in the history of motoring.

I give a start when the Police Inspector suddenly speaks: "Have you been told that I would ask you to drive that way?"

"Yes," I reply, "and wasn't it a good turn?"

"It was a left turn," Police Inspector Sorensen says. "I told you to turn to the right."

"Oh, goodness! I'm awfully sorry. Shall I turn back?"

Herr Sorensen doesn't think I should. We proceed up and down horrible little side streets in silence. Left, right, right, right, left, left . . . I pay at least twenty hasty return visits to the dancing school, I squeeze the memory of Gustav's hand and am quite exhausted from lifting my right foot up high before we arrive in Abel Catherine's Street, where five learners' cars scatter at the sight of me and Sorensen approaching to turn around.

I pull up at the curb in Puggaardsgade (Pug Farm Street) to discuss the theoretical side of motoring with Sorensen. "What would you do if the steering wheel didn't work?" asks the police inspector.

"Phone for help," I reply.

"Can you tell me anything about the brakes?" Sorensen asks.

No motor mechanic in Copenhagen is able to talk at such length about brakes as I am today. All Enok's axioms flow unhindered from my lips.

As we return to the sidewalk where we left Enok, Sorensen's face is still an expressionless mask. Enok starts bowing as soon as he catches sight of the car.

"Passed!" says The Examiner.

"Thank you very much, Herr Police Inspector," says Enok.

"That's *fine and dandy*, Sorensen," say I.

But Sorensen has already left us, as silent and brooding as when he came.

"A fine man," says Enok.

I returned in triumph to our summer residence where Ellen was waiting with the children expecting to hear that I had flunked. When she heard that I had passed, she reckoned her own future as bright and full of promise. She didn't know when it would be her turn, but Enok promised to call and take her out for a final lesson as soon as he knew how things were.

The following Monday we heard the noise of Enok's car outside. He didn't sound his horn as usual. Even at a distance I could see that he was the harbinger of bad news. The carefree smile was no longer on his lips. As he walked toward the house his steps were heavy and he dragged his feet. His eyes were dull and full of sadness.

"Is Liebergut dead?" I asked. It was the saddest thing I could think of on the spur of the moment.

"No," he said. "It's about the other little lady. I can't help it—she's to be examined by Herr Stiefelbaum!"

"*Stiefelbaum!*" Ellen and I repeated, and it came from our throats like a scream of horror. I looked at my unhappy friend, the woman with whom I had gone through so much, this gentle creature deserving of a kindlier fate. Herr Stiefelbaum!

Gentle readers who are over thirty years of age all know of Herr Stiefelbaum. He was the police examiner who, during a whole generation, was mentioned with the same terror as the twelve plagues of Egypt, as the earthquake in San Francisco, as the tidal wave at Norderney. He was one of Nature's major catastrophes. This was the man beside whom my Sorensen and my sister's Skrappenborg were gay, talkative, lovable boys. He was the man who never said hello and never goodbye. He was the man who could find streets to turn in that were so narrow that anyone equipped with a modicum of common sense would not attempt to turn even a bicycle around in them.

He was the man who laid the most malignant traps and who considered the day spoiled if he, much against his will, had been obliged to pass a pupil and issue a driving license. This was the man who had no fixed route and who could ask questions about things that were not only not mentioned in the book, but which no normal God-fearing motorist had ever heard of.

Enok and Ellen drove around in Copenhagen for a whole day and caused chaos by trying to turn the car around in all the narrowest streets they could find. And the next day Ellen went bravely to meet her fate.

Herr Stiefelbaum bade her drive into Pustervig (Windy Creek Street) and turn the car around in the exact place where a barrow piled high with carrots was parked. Ellen said afterwards that she was sure Herr Stiefelbaum had paid the boy to park there with his barrow, thus making the narrow street even narrower.

However, as soon as Ellen had slightly grazed a single carrot with a promontory of Enok's battered vehicle, thereby causing a couple more to roll off into the street, Herr Stiefelbaum asked to be allowed to descend.

As he set foot to the ground he unfortunately trod on a carrot and sprained his ankle and was obliged to ask to be allowed to get in again.

Enok, who had been trembling as with the ague in the rumble seat, had to take over the wheel and drive them back. Ellen claimed afterwards that Herr Stiefelbaum clearly regretted that he was not in a position to fail Enok.

Herr Stiefelbaum did not thank them for the ride.

A month later Ellen tried again. This time she drew a luckier number in the driving-license lottery, and passed the test. The interlude with Herr Stiefelbaum had been too short to mark her for life. On the contrary, she later admitted that she was grateful for this experience, for it had provided her with a subject of conversation that she could use at any time and in any company.

If a party is bogging down, or if someone starts to divide the room with an East-West debate, she mentions Herr Stiefelbaum. When somebody asks an embarrassing question, such as "Is your child doing well at school?" she quickly lets drop the fact that *she* was once examined by Herr Stiefelbaum. It is not unlikely that Ellen will talk her way into Heaven by regaling St. Peter with tales of Herr Stiefelbaum— who is obviously a candidate for some other destination—and so will I.

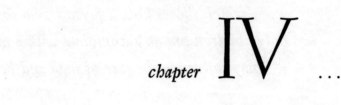

chapter IV ...

*. . . which shows how a person who shares
not only children but an automobile with a man,
may influence the fate of man and beast.*

You can say what you like about my husband, but this I *will* say for him: he took my acquisition of a driving license like a man. He even wrote a letter to my father explaining the circumstances that had led to his abandoning of the family principles.

To his friends he remarked that it was, all told, most practical if one's wife could drive a car.

There could be moments when her ability to drive could be to the advantage of both husband and car— not to mention other users of the road.

This assertion stood its only trial one evening after we had been to a party at the home of some of our friends. Peter—who had stated that he was going to drive us there and back as usual—sat over his after-dinner coffee wearing a silly grin on his face and talked with fuzzy S's and large gestures.

When the highballs made their appearance I said, from force of habit and in my most wifely voice, that my husband didn't want any more as we were driving home.

Peter sent me a cross-eyed look, raised his glass, and said:

"May I take the libershy of shuggeshting that we drink the health of *Liebergusch?*"

None of the others knew who Liebergut was. But that was of no consequence. Some guessed that this must be the secret pet name of our hostess, and several of the guests shouted that Peter was always so considerate and here's to Oda, our hostess with the mostess, whom it is always such a pleasure to guest.

I alone realized that the hour had struck. For the first time I was going to drive our own car with my husband as passenger.

As we were leaving I did wish, however, that Peter resembled the man I had married a little more. He slumped into the front seat and waved the ignition-key uncertainly in front of the dashboard.

"Thank you," I said acidly, "I can manage. But I would be grateful if you would show me where the lights are?"

Peter pointed with a grandiose gesture to a knob and told me to pull it out.

"It doesn't sound like Enok's car . . ." I said doubtfully.

"Firsh gear," said Peter. "Thash ri'. And now the other gear, my schweet!" He leaned against me.

"Stay in your seat! I'm not used to having someone hang over me—especially not someone with a breath like yours," I said.

"There'sch a car coming t'warsch usch," Peter informed me. "Now thir' gear."

"I can manage," I said.

"Don't lesh tha' taxschi crowd you," Peter advised as we were overtaken. "After him . . . !"

"No," I said.

"Schtep on it!" Peter rooted. "Someone'sch going to overshtake usch again."

But we weren't overtaken. We were stopped. A policeman put his head through my window. He must have had an unusually poor sense of smell because he didn't withdraw his head at once and gasp for air.

"Your headlights aren't on," he said.

"That's funny," I said. "I know I put them on."

Peter peered at the dashboard, and I prayed that he wouldn't exhale.

"You've pulled out the schoker instead," he said reproachfully, shook his head slowly, and looked at the policeman. "Women!" Peter said and smiled in a brotherly way at the head in the window. The head smiled back.

"May I see your driver's license, ma'am?" asked the policeman.

I knew exactly what was in my party purse: comb, lipstick, powder compact and handkerchief. There isn't room for anything more in my party purse. But I opened it and rummaged dutifully for the license. Full of amazement I said:

"It isn't here! I must have forgotten it at home. And it's a brand-new one, too."

"Hm," said the policeman.

"Now isn't that strange!" said I.

The policeman regarded me suspiciously.

"Doesn't your husband have a license?"

"Yes, but . . ."

I didn't get any farther before Peter had pulled out his disreputable old license. The policeman looked from the confidence-inspiring countenance that graced this document to the doltish mug on the man at my side. And not only must his sense of smell have been practically nonexistant, but he must have been afflicted with bad eyesight as well. Because he said:

"Well, that's fine then, why don't you change places with your husband?"

He gallantly opened the door for me, whereupon Peter crawled over and sat himself behind the wheel.

"But . . ." I said.

With a gesture the like of which I had never witnessed before, Peter leaned over and opened the opposite door for me.

"Schtep right in, my schweet!" he said.

Convinced that the policeman, on top of all his other afflictions, must have been nearly deaf as well, I sank back in the upholstery. Peter started the car and waved to the arm of the law which was raised in a brotherly farewell from the roadway.

"A perfec'ly scharming p'leesch'm'n," my husband said.

"Stop at the first cab stand," I said, "and we'll take a taxi home."

Peter was quite unable to understand why we should go to such lengths of luxury. With sibilant speech and lordly gestures he explained that he was perfectly able to drive. Which the police had told him to do anyway. He was willing to prove to anybody that he was perfectly able to drive a little growler like ours through the silent, nightly streets. He would also gladly back a heavy truck and trailer onto a ferry, and a busload of tourists over the Matterhorn . . .

While he made this last impressive statement two of our wheels were up on the sidewalk, but as far as I know there are no sidewalks on the Matterhorn, and so I omitted to remark on it. But I did draw his attention to a car that was trying to overtake us, and I remarked that the driver seemed to be a bit nervous about it.

"He doeschn't have to go any farscher 'n us," Peter decided and barely missed a cyclist.

"Devil take all schyclischsts!" Peter said. And then we were home and all our little children could thank a benevolent fate that they were not orphans.

When we were in bed Peter waxed sentimental. He let his thoughts go back to Liebergut.

When one considered what a beautiful and promising and valuable animal it had been, it was surprising that Enok hadn't taught me a bit more about the layout of a dashboard. Imagine not being able to see the difference between the choker and the headlights. And hadn't Enok told me that I must never let a taxi crowd me?

"Isch firsch law o' motoring," Peter said. "If you don't even know that I won't let you drive me home from partiesch any more . . ."

"I hope you mean that," I said.

That was the last time Peter drank Liebergut's health at a party. And I never became our family's party chauffeur. But I did surprisingly quickly learn to handle the car in normal city traffic.

When, over a number of years, you have ferried an ever increasing number of children about on the simple vehicle known as the bicycle, you only have to pack four children and a dog into an automobile once to realize that old Henry Ford was a pretty smart fellow. Everything is much simpler when kids and purchases can be dumped together in a box on wheels.

It was interesting, too, to observe the transformation that took place in my greengrocer when he discovered that I had suddenly become motorized.

Through the years he had looked on passively while I stowed children and roots and herbs and fruit on my bicycle, not deigning to move an inch from his fixed place behind the counter. Not even if he saw that I was having trouble finding room for a last child or bunch of rhubarb. With lethargic eyes he and his wife had looked on while I chased potatoes, cauliflowers and small children that fell off and rolled every which way.

But now all this is changed.

The day I rolled up in Peter's car—which was now also mine—and parked at the curb that hitherto had supported only my overworked bicycle, both the greengrocer and his wife underwent a sudden and marked metamorphosis.

I was now promoted to the category of customers who were incapable of carrying even the smallest package themselves. Could this have been because a glance at my car showed the greengrocer that it would be the easiest thing in the world for me to proceed the three hundred yards that separated his store from that of his nearest competitor in the neighborhood?

From that day I never carried so much as a sprig of dill across the sidewalk. The greengrocer and his wife almost fought for the honor of going out and putting it in the trunk compartment of the car. My dumbfounded children were presented with plums and green peas whenever they condescended to leave the car and follow me into the store.

Our dog, who had hitherto been ignored and even unwelcome, now on several occasions received a pat on the head and a smoked herring.

If I happened for once to turn up on my old bicycle it was regarded as a democratic jest, just as when

Princess Margrethe rides by tram or the King takes off his coat when shooting the popinjay. On such democratic occasions I was accompanied to the curb, where my purchases were arranged like garlands on handlebar and carrier.

Things had changed indeed.

Under these circumstances it will be readily understood that I didn't feel much like letting Peter use the car for his everyday transportation. My life had been made easier at one stroke. In fact things would have been quite ideal if the children hadn't been afflicted with a hereditary taint from their father.

Outwardly Peter is a peaceful, kindly man. Faced with difficulties, he knows what a wife is for. If it is necessary to complain to the landlord about nightly noises on the stairs, or if painful problems have to be discussed at a parents' meeting in the school, he considers it quite in order to remain at home while I go and express the strong views he has entertained me with before I leave.

If a strange man appears on our doorstep and complains that his maiden aunt has been run down by one of the children on a bicycle, Peter doesn't even bother to present himself, let alone occupy himself with the complaint. Instead he calls his wife in a tone of voice so plaintive that anybody who doesn't know him must perforce think that he has been struck by some sudden indisposition.

As soon as I appear at the door to face the problem on the mat, Peter makes himself scarce and reappears only when the coast is clear. And then he always knows exactly what I should have said and done.

He hears me like a schoolmaster and considers my faltering contribution to these weighty problems of the day, after which he goes over the whole matter again, spicing it with his intelligent and grave reflections, mordant comments, considered conclusions, unwavering decisions. Thus and thus the matter should have been handled, Peter says, and I have no doubt that he is right.

Peter never gives himself a chance to display his faculty for putting people in their place. But when we go out driving he rehabilitates himself.

He has a name for anybody and everybody that gets in his way and in his hair. It would be possible to publish a weighty encyclopaedia of Peter's special appellations for other users of the road.

Drivers who do not immediately press their cars right into the gutter, when Peter wishes to overtake them, are usually addressed as *Road-owner Olsens, Low-gear Larsens, Squatter Sorensens*, and so forth.

Drivers who start to overtake before Peter has overtaken them are *Mental Deficients* and *Drunken Degenerates, Mashers, Misfits* and *Dope Addicts*.

Pedestrians who get the demented idea of stepping

into the roadway when Peter is in the vicinity, are called *Decrepits, Subnormals, Pedigangsters* and *Traffic Toads.*

I will abstain from putting down what all cyclists are labeled, because it would be struck out by the censor in any case.

The same applies to Peter's display of verbal gymnastics whenever a taxi comes near him. It may be noted, however, that all drivers of square delivery trucks are uniformly known as *Box Bastards.*

This is but a small selection of what Peter says when he drives, while his utterings percolate into eight eagerly cocked little ears.

He often treats us to the dazzling speech he dreams of making to the Minister of Justice. Peter is sure that his arguments would lead to an immediate revision of the traffic laws.

Peter has another speech which he is reserving for that unlikely time in some nebulous future when he will meet up with Chief of Police Vagn Bro, that well-known advocate of the speed limit, to whose theories Peter heartily subscribes as applying to all his enemies on the road—but not, of course, in the case of the practiced driver, which—by a strange coincidence—means Peter himself.

No child listens in vain to such a father.

As time went by and my issue gained the power of

speech, they lived up to the proud traditions and undertook the task of spreading Peter's gospel to a wider forum.

The first words our twins learned to say were not the lovely words "Mommy" and "Daddy," but "Misfit" and "Moron." These expressions were not used at family gatherings but exclusively in or near pedestrian crossings.

Our youngest daughter was scarcely eighteen months old when she—in a voice unusually powerful in one so young—was able to shout *Road-owner Olsen* at unoffending drivers; and our eldest son became a master at illustrating his father's epithets by making faces, threatening gestures and thumbing his nose at the roadhogs we passed on our whirlwind way.

The children had some difficulty in getting used to having me drive. Besides manipulating the car I concentrated on admonishing them not to fight among themselves, on trying to teach the dog not to sit on the brake pedal, on turning around and dragging children down from the package shelf in front of the rear window. Seeing them there is so confusing when what you want is a glance at the traffic behind you.

But for the children it was but poor fun to be restricted to such entertainment as they were able to devise within the walls and windows of the car.

They were used to better entertainment and saw no reason why their father's beliefs should be kept from the world just because he was prevented from being present.

And so it came to pass that I drove about with four children who through open windows broadcast their opinion of the people who had the temerity to use the road at the same time as we.

My way was heralded with slanderous *Mental Deficients*, *Box Bastards*, *Traffic Toads*, *Main-liners* and even worse utterings I regret to say, which in consideration for the aforementioned censor, cannot be repeated here.

It will be readily understood that my drives were anything but dull. I have sometimes felt sorry for the motorists who daily travel great distances with no other entertainment than that provided by the radio.

To the gay life in our small car must be added yet another adventurous factor of which my husband is the direct cause.

I don't know which questions the police examiner posed my husband when he took his test many years ago. They certainly cannot have been questions having anything to do with the insides of the car. If they had Peter wouldn't have passed the test, for his knowledge of what makes a car go is restricted to this:

He knows how to open and close the doors and windows, how to shift the front seat forwards and backward, how to change gears, where the brake pedal and handle are, and how to find the hole in the back where the gasoline goes in. He has also found the hole where the radiator-water goes in, and in the book of instructions he found in our Taunus when we bought it, he has read that the tire pressure should be twenty-four.

He bandies this figure about all over gasoline stations in an authoritative voice, leaving nobody in any doubt that he—if the fancy should take him— would be quite capable of taking the whole automobile apart and putting it together again in record time.

This impression is further strengthened by his habit of getting out of the car when buying gasoline, and closely watching the attendant's every movement.

While a queue of cars forms behind us, waiting to be served, Peter asks to have the hood opened. He then stands and stares intently at the engine, fiddles with a cable here and a coil there and gets oil on his fingers so that all may see that he has a built-in genius for mechanics. After which he grandly states that everything seems to be in order, which the rest of us devoutly hope too.

He then walks once around the car while the attendant closes the hood, this being a job that needs a certain knack—a knack that Peter unfortunately does not possess, as was once revealed in the most humiliating way.

The attendant, a ruthless man with no sense of

service, went straight to the next customer and left Peter staring broodingly at his engine.

When the situation—which consisted of four automobiles waiting their turn to move up to the high-octane pump—at last demanded that we be on our way, Peter took hold of the hood in order to close it. There came a series of awful crashes, followed by a billowing movement of the car which caused the children to bang their heads against the roof and the dog to jump out of the window in blind panic. But the hood remained unclosed until our youngest daughter came to her father's aid, and with a sure and firm grasp of her chubby little hands, closed the recalcitrant lid.

We never entered that particular gas station again. Peter considered writing a complaint to the company, but gave it up and changed brands instead.

Peter's ignorance of the insides of an automobile makes him the mechanics' favorite customer. When he has driven the requisite number of miles before the regular check-up, he blithely rolls into the workshop. The car may be healthy and sound, free from rattles, well greased and full of gas when it arrives, but into the workshop she goes anyway. It is exactly like hospitalizing a person when there is nothing the matter with him.

When we get the patient—I mean the car—back and see the bill, we realize that it was indeed a white-washed sepulcher, a dangerous crock, a hopeless wreck that would have broken down completely if we had tried to go another two miles in it.

The healthy person who, being of sound mind, puts himself in the hands of a doctor will learn that he has been tottering along on the edge of the grave, with frustration in his soul, myosis in his limbs, tar in his lungs, and every variety of derangement known to science in his intestines.

Likewise the diagnosis that can be deduced from the repair bill shows that our car was ready for a change of several cylinders, gaskets and screws, of batteries and chromium whatnots. Even the tank— for some inexplicable reason—always has to be filled up again. Making the car fit to go has necessitated the emptying of the tank.

The bill tells how skilled mechanics have spent days under the chassis, welding the sorry pieces together again, and the figures show how busy little apprentices have been kept busy with our sad case for more hours than some of them can count without help from the foreman.

Pale but composed Peter checks through this medical certificate and its inevitable conclusion, namely that he owes the workshop at least two hundred kroners. But when these are paid, he firmly believes that no harm can befall his car again before it has gone the next specified number of miles.

Peter never doubts that his automobile really has been infested with all the ailments listed on the bill, and he also never doubts that nothing untoward will happen before the time for the next check-up is at hand.

Not that Peter doesn't notice it when a headlight fails or the gasoline gauge goes on strike. He just doesn't consider it important, inasmuch as the foreman, by cashing the check, has okayed the car. He rarely finds it necessary to mention such trifling ailments to me.

This is a state of affairs that gives a special fillip to my motoring. What is more surprising, when you start your husband's car in the morning, than a noise like six tin cans jumping about somewhere under the hood? And what is so encouraging as being able to get the car to go despite this—and to get the tin cans to remain silent until the next time you start up the engine?

If I tell Peter about this he receives my news with the same air of superiority as any other man whom you tell something he knows already.

"Oh, I know," he says, "but it's nothing to worry about. After all, the car was serviced only a fortnight ago."

Peter ignores strange noises. He knows it will cost the same whatever state he delivers it in for the check-up. Whether he comes gliding in like a snake on velvet, or whether he makes more noise than a formation of armored trucks, the diagnosis will be the same.

This makes for a sense of stability in Peter's existence and lots of excitement in mine.

When the children and I return home and tell how we spent an entire afternoon looking for a hubcap that jumped off on the Horsholm Highway, Peter goes us one better by revealing that he has hunted the same hubcap several times on the same highway.

And if we tell him how we had to stop because smoke and steam were coming out of the top of the radiator while water came out of the bottom, he is also unimpressed. Nothing can surprise him or shake his calm. He will explain that he himself had noticed that the car wasn't able to hold its water, but all this will be fixed when Foreman Johansen at the workshop gets his hands on it next time in three or four weeks.

One of the things that Foreman Johansen has never succeeded in getting under control is our gasoline gauge. Peter has his own system of telling how much gasoline is left in the tank. When he buys gasoline he puts the trip-counter back to zero, and when the car has gone upwards of three hundred and thirty miles he knows it's time to fill her up again.

It must be said in Peter's defense that this system worked very well for a couple of years—right up to that starry winter's night, in fact, when the car suddenly stalled on the only deserted stretch of road between Koge and Copenhagen.

The speedometer stood at two twenty-seven. But even Peter had a feeling that the tank was dry.

Especially as he was able to reveal that exactly the same thing had happened the week before. Only then it was on Falconer Avenue.

While the children and I huddled with chattering teeth in the car, Peter and the dog walked along the silent road under the twinkling stars towards the nearest gas station. I have always thought of the Koge highway as bordered with gasoline stations, but all of a sudden there wasn't one for miles.

Peter and the dog returned an hour later with a three-gallon can. He managed to get one gallon into the tank, the balance dribbling onto the road.

After which we continued home. But Peter never was one to bear a grudge. The next day he had the tank filled and put the speedometer back to zero and trusted that everything would be all right again and that Foreman Johansen would fix it in due course if it wasn't.

That was the week I had promised to drive three of my friends to a hen party in the suburb of Gladsate (Happyscissors).

All the way there we talked about how nice it was to have a car. At the well-decked table several alcoholic cheers were shouted for my driver's license and for Peter's car, while I, feeling honored and horribly sober, sat and received the plaudits of my friends.

It was midnight when my three friends, deliriously happy, and I, dead sober, got into the car to return home.

It rained in Happyscissors and it was pouring down when we reached Norrebrogade (North Bridge Street) in Copenhagen. We had just passed Slanger-upbanen (Snake Camp Station) when the car seemed to go weak at the knees. It said *"Phut!"* two or three times, after which it stopped with the sound I remembered from Koge highway. The speedometer said two-seventeen.

When you are in a hurry there is no limit to the density of the traffic in North Bridge Street. Now, all of a sudden, there was no traffic. The last *"Phut!"* from the engine seemed to be a signal for the rain to increase. It was now pouring cats and dogs.

We were apparently parked in a river, and my three happy passengers—who had been singing the traditional songs of our homeland ever since we left Happyscissors—went into "Sailing up the River," and left it to me to get out of the car and seek help.

In a side street fifty yards further on I spied a taxi about to start. I yelled "Help!" and "Hey!" and whatever else it is one yells at such a moment if one is a woman in distress. A small man with a pointed nose stuck his head out of the window.

"Sorry, ma'am, finished for today!" he said and was about to make off.

"Haven't you got a little gasoline?" I asked.

"Only in the tank, and I can't get that out," said the man.

"Well, can't you take me to the nearest gas station,

then? There are three unfortunate women sitting in my car along there."

The man didn't feel much like it.

"You see I promised my wife that I'd hurry home with this," and he held up a drugstore package. "For the stomach," he added portentously.

I suggested that we could go to his wife first and to a gas station afterwards.

He still looked doubtful, but something told me that he could be pursuaded, so I got in beside him.

"We have to go this way first," he said. "Then we'll find a gas station."

"That's quite all right, Herr . . . ?"

"Herr Mortensen," he said.

I assured him that I would know how to recompense his kindness—I and the three unhappy women.

We passed my car at that moment, and I could hear the unhappy women singing the lament of the Volga Boatmen.

A little later we stopped outside a building.

"It's on the ground floor," he said, "I shall probably only be a moment."

A quarter of an hour later Mortensen had not yet returned. There was a light in the apartment on the right, and I could see shadows moving against the blind. I began to think that Mortensen had found his wife gravely ill and that he had forgotten us.

After waiting twenty minutes I switched off his engine, and after half an hour I took out the ignition key and went into the building, certain that Mortensen's wife must be at death's door with her stomach, and that Herr Mortensen might need the help of an active woman.

I found the door of the ground-floor apartment standing ajar. I pushed it open expecting to find a feeble and suffering human being in the arms of her unhappy husband. Instead I found myself staring at the quivering back of an enormously fat woman in a night dress.

She was blocking the door to the living room, and under her raised right arm I caught sight of the trembling Herr Mortensen.

"Here you leave me weak and helpless while you go gallivanting around with women, you bastard!" Herr Mortensen's wife was saying.

"But, Little Mouse, I assure you, it's an elderly lady, in fact it's a very old lady, and she has three other old ladies waiting in her car, and we were going to fetch some gasoline . . ."

"You'll stay right here!" shouted the weak and helpless woman in a voice that could now be heard three blocks away. "When I think how ill I am, and what a state our home is in . . ."

Herr Mortensen, whom I could still see under her arm, opened his mouth, probably to make me even older . . .

"But, Little Mouse . . ."

"Shut up, you undersized night-owl!" screamed the patient and took a step towards him.

I came to the conclusion that my life was in danger, and prepared to retreat. As I turned around in the small, dark hall I failed to take into account that the Mortensen home was not quite as shipshape as it should have been.

I have always considered the location of the ironing-board as the criterion of a housewife's abilities as such. An ironing-board that remains hidden from human eyes when not actually in use makes her a Grade-A housewife.

If it hides behind a cupboard or such, where it can only be glimpsed by chance, the housewife is placed in Grade B. Grade-C housewives are the ones that keep their ironing-board in the bath, behind a door, or in the toilet or even larder.

Quite beyond the pale are the women who can't be bothered to fold it together and put it away between use. These are the women who leave it at random in fortuitous places to be fallen over by the unwary. Mortensen's wife belonged in this category.

Her ironing-board spanned the small hall, as I discovered when I hurtled it on my head. The angry woman in the doorway turned and looked at me with eyes that could have tamed an entire snake farm.

I felt that some sort of presentation was necessary.

"I am the lady from the car—I was afraid you

were very ill," I said breathlessly, picking myself up.

Fru Mortensen ignored my presence.

"If she's old," said Fru Mortensen to her husband, "then I'm a bloody old-age pensioner!"

"But, Little Mouse . . ." Herr Mortensen began.

"I'm much older than I look," I explained. "You see, I've run out of gas. My husband has forgotten to fill up the tank . . ."

This wasn't quite in accordance with the facts, but it was the simplest explanation. The moment was not propitious for a more involved narrative.

At the sound of the words "My husband has forgotten . . ." Fru Mortensen's attitude towards me became almost human. She let her enormous bulk sink into a moth-eaten armchair and said resignedly:

"Men are bastards."

Considering that an hour had passed since I had last heard the mournful strains of the Volga Boatmen from my abandoned car, and considering that Herr Mortensen's wife was still in danger, and considering that Peter was comfortably asleep in his own bed while I stood in a nasty ground-floor apartment in the middle of a family row at one-thirty in the morning, and considering that it was raining harder than ever and that I was wearing my best clothes and that I hadn't seen another taxi since my car went on strike—I decided that it was wisest to echo Fru Mortensen's sentiments, even though I do not think that men are bastards—not all of them.

"Yes," I said in a longsuffering voice, "it's awful what we women have to put up with."

That was the signal for Fru Mortensen to give me a detailed breakdown of her married life. While Herr Mortensen grew smaller and smaller her injuries grew bigger and bigger.

He was away all day, the little runt, and he called himself a taxi-owner, a man of means—yet didn't she have to make do with a measly seventeen-inch television set while Fru Andersen up on the second floor—whose husband was only a bricklayer—had a twenty-one-inch set, *and* he'd given her a calfskin coat for Christmas, and what kind of a present had she, Fru Mortensen, got?

In other circumstances I might have protested that it hardly seemed likely that so many innocent calves, as would be necessary to cover her vast expanse, should be slaughtered at once. But I now wanted so badly to see my abandoned car and my just as abandoned friends again that I willingly passed up the opportunity to air my feelings. I just shook my head in sympathy while Fru Mortensen went on.

During a detailed description of her ailment—a kind of pressure in her intestines—that occurred mainly when Fru Mortensen "allowed herself to eat a proper meal for once," Fru Mortensen stopped to take a breath.

I seized the opportunity to ask if I might use her

phone to call a taxi, because it was quite obviously
Herr Mortensen's duty to stay with her.

As though it had been Herr Mortensen who had
given me this impression, Fru Mortensen turned to
her husband and asked what the hell he was standing
there for? Wasn't he supposed to be going to get
some gasoline, and what was the idea of keeping the
lady waiting . . . ?

With mutual assurances that men were bastards,
Fru Mortensen and I took leave of each other.

"You certainly knew how to handle my wife," he
said admiringly as we set course for an all-night station.

"A very strong-minded woman, your wife," I
said carefully.

"She's a fat slob and a bitch."

We drove in silence through the rain. Then Herr
Mortensen said:

"She was a honey right up to the moment she had
me hooked. Ever since we were married she has sat
in the room behind her mother's shop and eaten cakes
and drunk coffee. Her mother keeps a junk-shop.
She is just like her daughter to look at, but she's not
so goddam lazy. Apart from that they're alike. Her
father was the clever one. He jumped in the harbor
when Alma was a little girl. Alma, that's my wife.
The water's supposed to be very dirty out there, but
he was the smart one all the same. I should have taken
a better look at her mother before I married Alma.

"Why don't you leave her?" I asked.

"I'm not saying that I won't one day," Herr Mortensen said. "Get myself a cute little baggage."

"There are plenty of them," I said encouragingly. "Plenty. You've only got to look in the right places."

"Fancy having a wife who could cook dinner—not just eat it," Herr Mortensen said dreamily.

Nobody goes unpunished for making me sit for half an hour in a taxi in a dark side-street in the northern outskirts of Copenhagen at one o'clock in the morning. I felt perfectly justified in undermining Fru Mortensen's position.

"If you only knew," I cajoled, "how many decent women there are in the world, women who are prepared to give a man a good, cozy home. And if anybody deserves such a home, Herr Mortensen, it's you . . ."

I was so moved by my own eloquence that I felt tears coming to my eyes.

"I could try an advertisement in the matrimonial column," said Herr Mortensen. "But I don't suppose it's easy to get rid of a wife like mine."

He probably had something there.

We got the owner of a gas station out of bed and drove back to my abandoned automobile with a five-gallon can.

The lament of the Volga Boatmen had long since come to an end. My three friends were huddled together in deepest sleep. The only thing stirring was the windshield wiper which I had forgotten to switch off.

I noticed that Herr Mortensen was able to get three of the five gallons into the tank. This time only two gallons were spilled on the ground. The strange events of the night had so dislocated my sense of proportion that I found myself thinking that Herr Mortensen, who was so good at fetching and pouring gasoline, deserved a better fate than Peter who had spilled half on the ground and still slept the untroubled sleep of the just at home in his bed, while his wife was in dire distress.

I took hearty leave of Herr Mortensen. "Now remember what I said!" I shouted as he drove off to rejoin Fru Mortensen.

"Many things will be changed," replied Herr Mortensen enigmatically and stepped on the gas.

I got into the car, and Lis, the girl in the front seat, woke up. She was a witness to my unavailing efforts to start the engine. During the hour and a half I had been gone the wipers had worn out the battery.

"We did think that thing ought to have been turned off," said Lis, "but to tell you the truth we couldn't find the switch."

I would become much too upset if I attempted to recall in detail all that happened before we got the car going again. It is enough to say that I was obliged to pay a visit to an all-night cafe and make friends with two gentlemen who should have been back home in the bosoms of their families long before that. They, in turn, solicited the help of the cloakroom attendant who, for a consideration, proved willing to help me get the engine going by pushing the car.

I gave Lis summary instructions in how to hold the car in second gear, and let go the clutch and step on the gas at the psychological moment. She assured me that she could manage this as easy as winking.

We pushed while rain and slush splashed us to the knees, and shouted "NOW!" to Lis, and then the car stopped. We proceeded in this manner down North Bridge Street almost to the Roundabout before it dawned on me that Lis might in some measure have misunderstood my instructions.

Right enough, it turned out that she had been stepping on the brake pedal instead of the accelerator. We were more than halfway home and had used no gasoline at all, before we finally got it going and I slumped in behind the wheel wet and tired.

We had scarcely got going before I noticed a strange, acrid smell in the car.

"Phew!" I said. "What on earth is that?" Lis, who had settled down in her corner once more, opened one eye and said that it was probably the cat.

"The cat?" I repeated.

Oh, yes, I hadn't been introduced to the cat, had I? It was wrapped up in the car rug, Lis said, and explained in a sleepy voice that Mille, who was a member of six different societies for the protection of animals, had caught sight of the poor cat on the sidewalk while the rain and the singing was at its highest. It was mewing strangely and it looked so helpless, and that was more than Mille's kind heart could stand. Face to face with an animal in distress she always knew the right thing to do.

"Are you sure it's not a skunk?" I asked acidly.

I stopped the car, put the light on, and wriggled around in my seat. There sat Mille fast asleep with the car rug folded and bulging in her lap, and apparently containing something as big as our poodle at home.

I lifted a corner of the rug and a pair of baleful green eyes glared at me. Never before had I seen so large a cat, nor a cat with such gigantic jowls.

"I think it's a tom," I said.

"Yes, now that you mention it, it does smell like that, doesn't it?" said Lis.

We stopped at Mille's address and she staggered out like a person drugged, leaving the cat behind her.

"You forgot something," I said.

"I know, but the awful thing is that I'm not permitted to keep animals in the apartment," she explained. "So if you don't mind . . ."

"No!" I said.

"But it'll only be until tomorrow—then I'll find a good home for it."

"No!" I said. Peter had a thing about cats, and anyway we had a dog.

Mille was completely awake by now. She stood by the door of the car and entertained us to a long discourse on kindness to animals. It was all a question of whether you had culture, she explained. And what was more, if you had a dog you ought to have a cat as well.

"But we've got birds too," I explained in the hope of making a good impression in protection-of-animals circles.

Mille turned to Tut, who had slept soundly ever since the cat was rescued, and shook her. "You believe in kindness to animals, don't you?" she asked her friend.

"Yes, but the cat wouldn't be happy with me," Tut maintained.

"Of course it would!" Mille insisted.

We sensed that Tut would go to any lengths not to become a cat owner. After much talking forwards and backwards with Mille, she finally resorted to blackening her inoffensive husband's character.

She lowered her voice and confided the awful truth about Holger.

He kicked cats.

"As for you, Lis, I wouldn't even ask you," Mille said offended. "You said just now that the cat smelled. That is quite untrue, and it shows that you have no feeling for animals."

After which she caught up cat and rug and disappeared into the building with a remark to the effect that it would be our collective fault if she was turned out of her apartment. But *she* wasn't the sort to desert poor, helpless animals.

It was after three when I got home. Peter turned sleepily over in bed and mumbled something about it being a bit thick having a gadabout wife who came tramping in at dawn and made a goddam awful din in the bedroom.

I took hold of his shoulder to shake him awake and give him a blow by blow account of my night on the town. I took a deep breath and got ready to keep him entertained for half an hour.

"The car stalled out on North Bridge Street. The tank was empty though the car had only gone two-seventeen miles . . ."

Peter wasn't interested.

"I'm not surprised," he said. "Nothing strange about that at all. I was giving Oluf a lift yesterday and he discovered that the brakes were jamming. No wonder. The workshop will have to see to them next time."

And with these words Peter pulled the eiderdown over his head without a second thought for the exhausted woman standing by his bed, dead beat and in need of understanding and sympathy and warmth and the milk of human kindness.

I lay awake a long time wondering whether Peter was the right husband for me.

The next day was heralded with a prolonged ringing of the front door bell, followed by the baying of our dog.

"The bell!" Peter mumbled as he always does. I usually go out and see who it is. But this time I pretended to be dead, and I know I wished I were.

At last Peter, taking his time and in the midst of the infernal noise of ringing bells, barking dogs and awakening children, got ready to go and see who could be ringing our bell at seven o'clock in the morning.

To prevent my being much better off than himself he left the door between the bedroom and the hall open.

Outside the front door stood a policeman.

"Are you the proprietor of motor vehicle number K 88.001?" he asked Peter.

Peter admitted that he was.

"You have at around two o'clock this morning taken unlawful possession of a four-year-old male cat answering to the name of Severin," the policeman announced.

"No," said Peter.

The policeman began to talk to Peter in the voice and manner I imagine young police officers are taught to use when addressing persistently obstinate criminals.

Peter must understand that there existed weighty circumstantial evidence; a young man and woman had certified that they last night had seen a lady jump out of the motor vehicle in question and appropriate the said cat, a household pet owned by Fru Karen Amalie Madsen domiciled in the same building as the aforementioned young persons. They had made a note of the license number of the automobile and had at once reported to its owner that the cat, whose name as has been mentioned was Severin, had been forcefully abducted. The lady had then immediately enlisted the aid of the police.

The children had formed a circle around their father. Through the open door I could see that my little family, thus arranged, resembled a front-page photograph in the newspaper "B.T."—one of those with a heart-rending caption such as: "The Courageous Little Family Just Before Its Dissolution," or "We want to keep our Daddy!"

"Just a moment," Peter said and retraced his steps.

I hurriedly pulled the eiderdown up over my head and pretended to be asleep.

"Where's the cat?" Peter asked ominously.

"Which cat?" I mumbled innocently, while in my mind's eye I saw Peter at police headquarters face to face with Fru Karen Amalie Madsen—a sight that filled me with unholy glee as I recalled what I had suffered from his recalcitrant automobile.

"My wife had the car last evening and night," Peter explained to the policeman.

"Is that so!" said the arm of the law in a tone of voice that meant that in that case, of course, anything was possible.

Peter turned once again to me. "Now," he said, "Where's the cat—the one you abducted."

"Oh, *that* one," I said brightly.

I felt that I had already lost the battle and that they would not carry off Peter this time. I also felt that I had better wake up properly and explain everything if *I* wanted to stay out of jail.

Our youngest child stopped crying as I passed the buck—in this case Severin the tom—to Mille.

I assured them that she had done it with the best of intentions, that she was a true animal lover, member of six societies for the protection of her dumb friends. At the mention of this a look of terror passed over the policeman's face.

"Gosh, save us from them!" he muttered.

"Anything can happen when a woman drives," Peter interjected, feeling superior again.

"Check!" said the cop. "Now take my sister-in-law . . ."

He and Peter went into a huddle about all the bad things that happen to an automobile which falls into a woman's hands.

The policeman, whose name was Rasmussen, stayed for breakfast and went on talking about women and automobiles with Peter, who finally offered to drive him over to Mille to fetch Severin.

As they left I sent up a fervent prayer that the engine might stall on the way, that they would have to push it to the nearest repair shop, and that this might be situated at a very great distance.

A week later the jamming brakes were unjammed. We soon forgot the annoyance they had caused us, because new and no less exciting episodes cropped up as a consequence of Peter's pathetic belief that no ill can befall any car that is serviced regularly.

My adventure because of the jamming brakes and the consequent increased consumption of gasoline was recalled to me a couple of months ago.

At a table near ours in Peter Liep's Restaurant in the Deer Park outside Copenhagen, a couple were seated. Peter drew my attention to the man who appeared to be trying to attract my attention.

I looked up and saw Herr Mortensen seated behind a cup of coffee and a small dry cake.

By his side, ensconced behind a gigantic piece of layer cake, sat a lady who was not the Fru Mortensen I knew. But she might have been her twin sister. She lacked only a few ounces.

Herr Mortensen got up and came over to our table.

After suitable greetings and introductions had been made, he whispered: "I took your advice as you can see. She was a honey when I met her two years ago ..."

"Congratulations, Herr Mortensen," I said.

"Mortensen!" yelled the lady at his table.

"Yes, Little Mouse!" answered Herr Mortensen nervously. "I'm coming . . ."

We could hear Herr Mortensen ordering another piece of layer cake for the lady.

When they left the waiter helped her on with her calfskin coat.

chapter V ...

. . . which is about how the omnipresent arm of the law can intrude on a woman's life, and about several kinds of parking attendants who intrude on her good nature.

The policeman's visit on the occasion of the abduction of Severin the cat was not to be my only skirmish with the police in my motoring career.

I don't know how the traffic cops of Copenhagen share the work between them, but I do know that one man—at least—is exclusively employed to watch my driving and to see how, and for how long, I park my car at curbs all over the city.

It began in quite a small way. It began, as a matter of fact, by other arms than those of the law sticking the little green and yellow slips we all know so well, on the windshield of the car.

During the first months after that memorable day when I demonstrated my skill and obtained my driving license from Police Inspector Sorensen, I had often found a printed greeting stuck under the windshield wiper.

Sometimes it said succinctly: "Car need washing? Try Carlo's Service Station." Or: "Do you need recovering? Lund & Larsen are experts." Once the slip said: "Jesus is coming tomorrow," and another time there was something about the hearty welcome await-ing me at a meeting, the purpose of which was to strike a final and decisive blow at our Exploiters. Who these were was not specified. But like all the other little slips it was simple, succinct, harmless.

Then suddenly a new and sad epoch was ushered in by a message I found stuck in the usual place. It said politely for me to phone a certain police station in the center of the city and ask for extension four and a Herr Lindeblad. The ticket made it clear that my car had been parked too long in Kattesundet (Cats' Sound Street).

The fact that Herr Lindeblad wished to know why the car had taken up space at the curb for more than three hours showed that he sensed there must be a logical explanation which would exonerate me from blame.

I was glad to know that I would be able to entertain him with one of the most gripping stories of everyday life that any policeman had ever heard.

I phoned Herr Lindeblad who turned out to be a man with a kindly personality. Introductions over, I threw myself wholeheartedly into the moving account of an altogether unsuccessful visit to my hairdresser. This had been prolonged by a full hour because an apprentice had forgotten to rinse the soap out of my hair.

"Have you ever had soap in your hair, Herr

Lindeblad?" I asked, and he replied that he could not recall such an instance, but that he didn't doubt that it was dreadful.

I described in detail how my tresses had been stiff as little sticks and how Monsieur Michel, who honored me by doing my hair, did not discover the calamity until the eleventh hour (or anyway the second) after which he, personally, almost in tears and with trembling hands, had rinsed out the soap and begged me not to let my circle of friends know that anything so awful had happened in his blue and gold salon.

I emphasized to Herr Lindeblad that it was only the exceptional situation in which I now found myself that was the cause of my disclosing the disgrace of the *Salon Michel*. I said that I counted on Her Lindeblad's discretion.

Herr Lindeblad assured me that not a word of this should pass his teeth.

I received the impression that he was a man of honor. His voice expressed much sympathy with the predicament in which I had found myself—especially when I came to the bit about my having been late with the dinner that day as a consequence of the business with the soap, and of course especially when he could hear that I had been absolutely devastated when I came down and saw to my horror that my car had been a hindrance to the traffic by being parked too long in Cats' Sound Street.

Peter sat in an armchair and listened to my phone

conversation with Herr Lindeblad. When I finished he grinned oafishly and said that he knew the police and that I could have saved my breath with all those daft explanations.

This wounded me deeply, not so much because it showed that Peter had no appreciation of the fact that I, through no fault of my own, had been placed in an exceptional and embarrassing situation, but because Peter—without knowing the details—had tried to poison my mind about Herr Lindeblad and the police. I felt that I had made a friend for life, of Herr Lindeblad, a gallant member of a band of fearless men to whom I knew I could always turn with confidence.

After my telephone conversation with Herr Lindeblad I came to the conclusion that it was entirely Peter's own fault that he had already received three tickets for overparking.

If he, in a polite and sincere manner, had told the police about his difficulties, things would not have come to such a pass, I said.

Next time I heard from Herr Lindeblad it was in the form of a very formal letter from which it appeared that the police would like to have forty kroners because I had parked too long in Cats' Sound Street.

This put Peter in such a high good humor that one would have thought the letter had informed us that the police were going to give *us* forty *thousand* kroners.

He insisted that I pay the fine out of my own pocket, and for a couple of days I saw no other way out but to take the money from a sum I had been saving for a new purse.

Then it was that I happened to notice that the letter said: *"Forty kroners or alternatively four days simple prison."*

Very few women have presented to them the power of escape from their often humdrum, always hectic, homes. And since it was nearly Easter, and I always spent Easter cooking and washing up and putting the food away and taking down dishes from shelves and cooking again and washing up and making coffee and washing up and so on, I decided to go to prison.

I looked forward to four wonderful days behind prison bars while Peter and the children took over the job of keeping the home fires burning and dishes washing. I had heard that one was allowed to bring one's own armchair to simple prison, and I was already considering whether to choose Peter's deep Chesterfield or my own wicker chair from the bedroom.

As soon as I revealed my intention to Peter he rushed down and paid the forty kroners. He is a cad.

My *contretemps* with Herr Lindeblad was the first of a long series of similar encounters with the omnipresent arm of the law.

Since the time when I told Herr Lindeblad about my soapy hair, there wasn't a police station in Greater

Copenhagen that hadn't heard equally heart-rending stories of how my car happened to have been parked a quarter or a half or even two hours too long in a time-limit zone.

I seem to be hunted through the streets like an outlaw. I rotate around blocks of buildings at half hours at a time, trying to find a hole into which a Taunus can be squeezed—and having finally found one it is always time to move the car again before one has had time to do one's errands.

My way through life is paved with yellow and green tickets on which crafty policemen have scribbled hasty invitations to more intimate telephonic—and financial—liaison.

My only consolation is that I have been instrumental in keeping up many a policeman's cozy home and making his lot a happy one. If there is roast duck on the table at Christmas, and if they are able to turn on the television in the parlor every evening, then the policeman's wife and all the little policeman's children ought to think of me who contribute so much to the department which pays the salary that makes these amenities possible. When at Midsummer and at Christmas the newspapers, with tears in their ink, invite their readers to give a mite for the good of the community—over and above the regular taxes—then I feel that I am well in the vanguard of philanthropy. Not that it isn't most laudable for people to take it on themselves to provide for a strange child for a day or two, but it is surely a far, far greater thing that I do, when I help to guarantee the policemen fathers of families steady work all the year round.

Just as the ever vigilant traffic cop is a factor the motorist must reckon with, so there is another phenomenon of our time that cannot be ignored: *the parking attendant.*

In Copenhagen, when the war ended and cars started crowding the streets, the problem of parking threatened to disorganize an otherwise well-organized city. In every public square or wide intersection drivers simply dropped their cars in more or less disorder, despite the threat of parking tickets.

Necessity being his mother, the Parking Attendant was born.

The position he occupies in the motorized community is much more interesting than the policeman's. The individual arm of the law is a man who has gone to some length to apply for and obtain his job. He receives his wages from the authorities, who in turn get them from us.

But with the Parking Attendant it is a case of pay—or else. The creation of Eve from Adam's rib is always mentioned as the simplest feat of genesis in the history of mankind. But I venture to say that the creation of a parking attendant is even simpler.

A man with little else to do, one day sees the disorder in a given area or square. Next day he arrives early wearing a visored black cap and an air of authority. He helps you park in orderly rows. He keeps others from blocking you. He helps extricate your car when you want it. At first he was grateful for gratuities, as you were for his help. As an unpaid guarantor of civic order, he was not only tolerated by the city, but encouraged. He grew and expanded and then—organized. So now when you leave your car he puts a numbered slip in the windshield wiper, gives you a copy, and charges a fixed fee—for allowing you to park your car on the city street.

No matter how mean his intentions may be, the policeman must always talk politely and obligingly and listen patiently to people's explanations, and dissolve traffic jams and other kinds of chaos as diplomatically as he can—for he must account for his actions to his superiors.

But the Parking Attendant is master of his own soul. He may be friendly and helpful if such is his natural disposition. But he can also let petitioners for parking space know that he is sick and tired of motorists and their cars, and that he would very much prefer that they get the hell out of there and find some other place to park for, Gawd knows, there's more of them than he can stomach.

As far as I have been able to ascertain there are three types of parking attendants. *Type A* is the one who runs his lot according to accepted business principles. If there's room, then okay, there's room;

and he is helpful and obliging irrespective of whether a long, sleek limousine or a jallopy that most of all resembles a wrought-iron sculpture by Robert Jacobsen, rolls into his domain.

He is equally nice whether he receives twenty-five ore or a whole kroner for standing and looking at the car, and in due course for directing its exodus.

Type B is the one who reminds you of the war days when certain goods were hard to come by in the stores, but when personal charm and female wiles could be bartered, for a joint of pork or two pairs of stockings, the nonexistence of which commodities the tradesman had begun by adjuring.

That was the time when a thrusting bosom and wiggling hips could work wonders; but that was the time, too, when it was sometimes possible to get results by simple flattery or by being a helpless little woman in distress.

The *Type B* attendant is the direct successor to all the storekeepers who had hard-to-get goods during the years of scarcity. On him one can still test one's power to beguile, and find out whether one's female charms have retained some of their potency. If they have, he will reshuffle his cars and find room for yours too. If they have not it will be practically hopeless to get a *Type B* attendant to take your car.

Finally there is the parking attendant *Herr C.* I write *Herr* from force of habit, because for years I thought that he—unlike his other colleagues—had actually *bought* the square where he reigned supreme.

Whether there is room or not, he it is who decides whether you may park your car. He can practically always find room for three or four more—but not just anybody's car. He has his regular clients, most of them people in very long cars, paid for by big expense accounts, and he is always prepared for the sudden arrival of one of them. And when that happens it would be regrettable indeed if a plebeian little car, paid for by its driver's hard-earned pay, should have the temerity to come chugging in and occupy one of the few costly spaces left.

Should the awful thing happen nevertheless, that an ordinary, common or garden-type motorist has occupied one of these reserved places while *Herr C* is otherwise occupied receiving a kroner from a driver who is taking his leave at the other end of *Herr C's* domain, *Herr C* will give such a display of oratorial fluency upon his return as would have made one of Hitler's speeches seem like a subdued bedtime story for neurasthenic toddlers.

With an irremovable cigar stuck in his face he lets loose a torrent of words while sparks and ashes fly about the face of the foolish driver who thinks that a public parking lot is for public use.

It happens now and again that a motorist stands on his rights and ignores both the ire and the fire and walks off with a smile of triumph on his face. But he only does that once.

When he comes back to fetch his car it will, quite by chance, have been scratched or dented. Or it will, again by coincidence, be locked behind a wall of other cars, a situation to which there are only two solutions. Either you give up all hope of getting your car back before all the other cars have left, or you enter upon negotiations with *Herr C*—in which case he not only triumphs in principle but also financially. You also give him a welcome opportunity to resume his fire-and-ashes discourse.

Herr C regards himself not only as the owner of the parking lot proper, but also of the narrow piece of roadway by which hopeful drivers approach it.

The entrance and exit to this roadway are situated at opposite ends of the parking lot, and thanks to *Herr C's* blessed labors one sometimes awaits one's turn in this queue for just as long as one had intended to park in the first place.

If *Herr C* happens to have absented himself for a short moment, and one of his regular customers turns up, then the car is simply left in the said roadway for *Herr C* to stow away upon his return. When this happens the car sits like a cork halfway down the bottleneck. And *Herr C*—having now returned—considers which cars he can best lay hands on and shove together, or which drivers he can most easily bully and frighten away in order to make room for his regular client's car.

The queue of would-be squatters steadily grows.

Some unrestrained individuals may make so bold as to sound their horns, after which, of course, it is their own fault if *Herr C* comes rushing up and blows fire and smoke in their faces and yells that there isn't any room and haven't they got eyes in their heads?

No wonder he hates these people and their cars as the queue grows in length and reaches out into the traffic lane. By their selfish behavior they are preventing *Herr C* from pushing his cars together. They show no understanding of the fact that he has been left with a large, black Mercedes to find room for, having received five kroners in advance to do so.

At such moments *Herr C* may be seen going in full blast. His blood pressure is up, his control down; his face is big and red and angry, his voice uncontrolled and his cigar erupting like Vesuvius.

He slings out threats that could form the basis for at least fifty cases of slander; he starts rows that in a less public place could result in mayhem and homicide. No Lord of the Manor, discovering that vulgar persons had parked their automobiles in his rosebeds, could wax more justly angry than *Herr C* when some dastardly person disputes his unrestricted right to the half acre of Copenhagen over which he has made himself master by the simple expedient of buying a cap with a shiny, black visor.

If I seem to dwell overlong on this last category of parking attendant, of which—so far as I know—there is only a single, but extremely virulent speci-

men, it is because *Herr C* was inadvertently instrumental in my sister Agnes' youngest daughter's laying
the foundation of her fortune.

It happened one spring morning that I, inspired
by an incorrigible optimism, and with my niece Tine,
aged ten, as my passenger, drove into *Herr C's* king-
dom, actually hoping to find him away and his more
amenable colleague in charge.

I immediately caught sight, not of a vacant space or
of *Herr C's* colleague, but of *Herr C* in full blast. He
had stuck his head and torso through the window of
an Opel Caravan in front of my Taunus and had apparently opened his heart to the lady at the wheel.
She was effectively prevented from fleeing, unless
she were willing to leave her car behind. In front of
her a large empty Buick, with open door and engine
running, was preventing anybody from getting past.

It appeared from the attendant's vociferous speech
that the lady had blown her horn, being of the completely erroneous opinion that she, if she couldn't
park her car, at least could expect to be able to leave
again taking her car with her.

But she wasn't *Herr C's* only problem. In front
of the Buick, in the space *Herr C* had intended for it,
there stood a tiny Fiat. This car proved to contain a
very large man who had the temerity to allege that
he had got there before the owner of the Buick and,
ipso facto, had first claim on the vacant space.

He got out of his Fiat and went up to the screaming

Herr C in order to acquaint him with the basic facts of the democratic rights of the people in this parking lot.

Herr C withdrew his head from the Opel Caravan and blew ashes and sparks at the owner of the Fiat. Words were bandied about the quiet lot, and I was becoming increasingly nervous that Tine, the innocent child entrusted to my care, should receive some permanent mental injury from being witness to so much discord, when I heard horns being sounded behind me. Three cars were waiting behind mine. Like me they were being prevented from proceeding by *Herr C's* verbal cataract.

I descended from my car in order to try and ascertain whether there was a chance that the altercation would last long enough to give me time to get to the store around the corner and purchase the six buttons which constituted the sum total of my errand.

By now everything was chaos in the parking lot. Nobody could get out and nobody could get in. *Herr C* seemed disposed to resume his labors, presumably so as not to miss a tip if a car should succeed in getting out without his help.

The situation was such that he would have to squeeze himself between the Opel Caravan and my Taunus in order to extricate himself from the jam of cars. He had just time to swear for a last time at the man in the Fiat when we heard a yell from his lips, and

it was as though a black cloud passed over his countenance.

He appeared to be stuck between the flat stern of
the Opel Caravan and the snout of my Taunus. Tine
had done what I would have liked to do. She had
released the handbrake of my car which pinioned
Herr C while he was attempting to slip between the
two cars.

There he stood, yelling louder than ever. I said
politely that he really must excuse us; the lady in the
Caravan stuck her head out of the window and remarked that children could be very wise and that they
had a great sense of justice; and the gentleman in the
Fiat emitted weird noises which made me afraid that
he was having a stroke but it was only convulsive
laughter.

When the row of cars behind mine observed that
we had advanced two feet they all did the same, while
Tine sat behind the wheel and screamed loudly in
fear.

I now had to back my car in order to release *Herr
C*. He turned his furiously red face towards me, and
I observed that his cigar had gone out. I smiled sweetly
at him and got to work. The cars behind mine were
obliged to relinquish the two feet they had gained
before the impaled parking attendant could be released.

Everything sorted itself out in good time. The
owner of the Buick came back, took his car, and drove

away. The rest of us occupied the spaces that had been vacated during the battle. *Herr C* disappeared, probably to look for mortal wounds for which he could claim damages.

Tine was still screaming and promised never to do it again. The lady from the Opel Caravan came and asked if the charming and intelligent little girl would like a great big ice cream cone.

While I was buying the buttons Tine went off with her new friend; and when I returned she was quiet and happy again.

"Look, Auntie, what the man gave me!" she said.

"That was the gentleman in the Fiat," the lady of the Opel Caravan explained.

Tine opened her child's fist, greasy from tears and ice cream, and displayed a crumpled fifty-kroner note.

"But you can't accept that!" I exclaimed. "It's quite out of the question."

"The man said I was to put it in my piggy bank," said Tine. "He said he enjoyed himself. Why did he say that. . . ?"

"That was because of the brake, my lamb," the lady of the Opel Caravan said.

"It's my money!" Tine asserted as though to prevent any misunderstanding.

It is on such a Spring morning that one suddenly feels the urgent need of a new hat. Just a cheap one at

say, seventy-five kroners—and that was exactly the amount I happened to possess.

A little later I was standing with a hat priced at one hundred and twenty kroners on my head, while the milliner gazed admiringly. I turned to Tine:

"Will you lend Auntie your fifty kroners till the first of the month?" I asked.

"I will if you give me back sixty," replied the child.

Thus Tine's flair for business was first revealed. It was later to astound her family and friends and acquaintances.

The sixty kroners were later loaned to her father who had to pay her back seventy. Since that time the money, or parts of it, has circulated among her sisters and brothers and cousins and has multiplied at criminal speed.

But on one occasion Tine's calculations went wrong. That was when, a couple of months after the episode in the parking lot, she climbed into her father's car, released the handbrake, and torpedoed her grandfather's new Vedette. To her immense surprise her bottom was thoroughly smacked by her mother who fined her a hundred kroners.

The occurrence gave my father a welcome opportunity to hold forth once more on the expediency of keeping women and cars separated.

chapter VI ...

. . . which is about how a motorist really lives in foreign lands among humans and dogs.

Peter and I had been to the movies, but I don't remember what film we saw. I do remember that we saw a publicity film for a certain expensive make of automobiles. One saw a distinguished married couple drive their car onto the seagoing motor ferry at Gedser in Denmark, and leave the ferry again at Grossenbrode, Germany, and drive out into the wide, wide world.

The wife was elegantly dressed in tight slacks and a large sweater, and she had a chiffon scarf tied around her hair. The husband was carelessly elegant in tweeds and Italian knitwear.

As we left the theater Peter said that it was really quite silly that we had never taken a streamlined vacation together. It was all right to spend a vacation with a dog and four children in a summer house in the country, but it would be nice, too, to go on a belated honeymoon and look nice and be well-dressed all the time. Just to enjoy life and laze about. To live in comfort and eat well.

I realized that the publicity film was still showing inside Peter's head. But anyway—why not?

The next day Peter went down to the motor club of which he was a member and returned with tourist folders from North Africa and Turkey. He seemed to think our car quite capable of taking us all that way and back in the two or three weeks we had at our disposal.

I explained that if we were to have a meal now and again and sleep even six hours every night, we would still have to average 100 miles an hour for the rest of the time. And even though Peter is an inveterate optimist where his car is concerned, he had to admit that the project presented some difficulties—taking into account the number of mental deficients and total idiots that got in the way of ordinary safe drivers like himself.

Next day he brought home folders from Austria, Northern Italy and the South of France, and a hotel list.

"I insist on a room with a private bath," I said. This seemed the height of luxury to me.

"Yes, of course we must have a private bath," Peter said. "And dance music on the terrace in the evening."

The children gathered around. They stood and leafed through the folders with lively interest.

"Great!" said Anders our eldest. "I've always wanted to climb the Alps."

"You're none of you going," I announced.

This piece of information was received with a look of disbelief as a bad joke. "Oh, don't be so silly," one of the twins said.

"You're all going to have a wonderful time at the seaside with Granny," Peter explained brightly.

"It is one thing," said the other twin, "that all the kids in our class have been to Spain and the Riviera, while we've only been to Malmo in Sweden and to Koge, because we have a summer house at the beach. We put up with that because we're original personalities. But you can't submit us to being left behind like that while you go abroad. Supposing we become ill, or drown? Suppose the dog runs away?"

"Do you honestly think you could enjoy such a vacation?" asked the other twin in a condescending voice. "What would Mother do if she received a cable in the middle of a Cha-Cha in Milano saying that her youngest daughter had broken her leg? Or if Dad received a phone call to say that the house had burned down?"

"You often hear of things like that happening," the other twin said gloomily. "But it's up to you, of course."

Anders remained stonily silent.

Peter gathered up the folders. The next day he

came home with a stock of new ones. They were all from a store that sold sporting goods.

"It's not true!" I cried when I saw what was in his mind. "You're not going to make me sleep in a tent?"

"It's not called sleeping in a tent," Peter explained to me. "It's called camping. If we take the three eldest children with us we must have tents. Staying in hotels would be too expensive."

"But we were going alone!" I wailed.

"Would you like to receive a telegram telling you about some accident?" Peter asked. "We can get somebody to look after Teeny and the dog, and we can lend the summer house to somebody who will tend the garden. After that we'll have nothing to worry about."

"Only about what we're going to use for money. Eating in restaurants comes high."

Peter gleefully took a folder from the pile. "Here's how we solve that problem. *Fixy, the portable kitchen.* We take along our own gas and cooking utensils."

The following days were spent trying to find somebody who would take Teeny while we were away. We sent her to my sister Agnete who tried her for one afternoon to see how they got on. "For," as she said, "it's so important how a child settles down."

The next day Agnete phoned and said that she didn't think Teeny could adapt herself to their life rhythm. During a single afternoon the child had demonstrated three variants of adjustmental distress. For one thing, she had released the canary and refused to participate in its recapture which had lasted three hours. While the family were bird-hunting she had played hairdresser and created a coif on her cousin Tine, as a consequence of which the poor child would start the summer practically bald. Towards evening Teeny had insisted on showing them a trick which consisted of pulling the cloth from the laid dinner table without disturbing the dishes. It hadn't worked.

It was apparent that Teeny had firmly made up her mind to go abroad with the rest of us.

"Oh, well," said Peter, "one more or less. All we've got to do now is put the dog in a kennel and off we go!!"

That evening Peter and I sat down to work out how much the camping equipment had cost us. We sent the twins off to arrange for Berta, our faithful poodle, to go into a kennel.

Peter had just worked out that we had bought 1085 kroners worth of tents, mattresses, portable kitchen, blankets, sleeping bags, night lamps, food boxes and waterproof covers, when Agnes and Benedicte came home.

"Nothing doing," they said.

"No room?"

"Yes, but we saw a dog standing tied up. It was crying . . ."

Anders said he couldn't understand why Berta had

to stay at home. Dogs could get passports. They just had to have a tetanus injection and a clean bill of health from a vet. If there was anything Berta needed it was to get out into the world and meet other dogs . . .

On the morning we left, Ellen and Henry moved into our summer house and promised to send us *poste-restante* postcards to let us know how things were.

Peter got in behind the wheel and our sixteen-year-old twins next to him. On the back seat our son, Anders, seventeen, Teeny, twelve, and I, were squeezed, while Berta took turns at lying down and sitting up on our various laps. The baggage compartment in the back was too full to close, and on the roof we had stacked the rest of the baggage so high that I had serious doubts as to whether all foreign viaducts would permit our getting through.

The sun was shining and our summer house had never looked more snug, roomy, beautiful or inviting than that morning in June when we waved goodbye as best we could, being hardly able to move our arms.

Never had the sun shone so brightly on Denmark and never had it rained so hard in Germany on one and the same day. It poured in Grossenbrode, it rained cats and dogs in Hamburg, and in Celle the rain was a flood of almost biblical dimensions.

"Don't let it worry you," Peter advised. "We'll just go on till we get to some dry weather."

At midnight we had journeyed far south and it was still pouring. The children slept, and Berta, who had to be let out at suitable intervals, smelled of wet dog.

"We'll stop at the next motor camp we get to," I decided. The next camp turned up half an hour later. Peter swung the car with his sleeping family in between long rows of tents. In nearly three hundred tents all was still and dark. From a single tent we heard gay voices.

"If I'm not very much mistaken," I said, "that's the song about the farmer who went out to fetch more beer. We are fallen among compatriots."

I do not remember how we got the tents up, the mattresses pumped up, and the children to bed. What I do remember is that I—for the first time since I was sixteen—went to bed without washing myself and brushing my teeth; went to bed is perhaps an exaggeration. Because just as I was about to crawl into my new, damp sleeping bag, I heard my mother tongue being spoken outside our tent, and a lady said "Yoohoo!" and then shouted a greeting in unadulterated Danish.

Peter opened the clammy flap of the tent. Outside stood a man in a bathrobe and behind him a voluminous woman with hennaed hair.

"The name is Aarslev. Nice to meet fellow Danes!" he said.

"I'm Fru Aarslev, but just call me Gurli!" shouted

the lady. I thought I recognized the soprano from "The Complacent Farmer."

"Pity you arrived so late," Herr Aarslev decided. "We've been having us a ball—we Danes, I mean. There's quite a little colony of us here!"

"The weather's not too good," Peter said like one imparting important news.

"I hear it's raining right down to the other side of the Alps," Herr Aarslev said cheerfully. "May as well sit in the rain one place as another."

"How about a beer?" asked the lady who had said that we might call her Gurli.

"Maybe they would rather wait until tomorrow," her husband said. "Tomorrow will be another day, Gurli. Can't you see they're tired? Well, *Gute nacht*, ha-ha! Must try to talk the lingo. . . !"

Aarslev was about to retire when he remembered something and turned to Peter.

"Golly, that's right! You've just arrived from home, haven't you? Then you'll know how the match between Frem and Koge ended?"

"Which match?" Peter asked.

"Frem and Koge," Aarslev repeated. "That was yesterday, wasn't it?"

"Yes, but what kind of match?" said Peter.

"Well, football, of course," I explained.

"Right, little lady, right! You're one of us!" said Herr Aarslev. He looked disbelievingly at Peter. "Well for cripes sake, you're not going to stand there

and tell me that you don't know whether Frem beat
Koge? Don't you read newspapers? Don't you listen
to the radio? Aren't you a sports fan?"

"Of course I am," Peter said weakly. "I—I play
tennis, you know. For the exercise."

"Tennis!" repeated Herr Aarslev. And once more:
"*Tennis. . .* !"

"Good night!" said Herr Aarslev, this time in
Danish.

"It was half-past seven next morning when Benedicte came crawling through the slit into the tent I
shared with Peter.

"Teeny's got such a funny big head," he announced.

"Rubbish!" I said. "I don't suppose Teeny's head
is any different from usual."

"You can hardly see her eyes, and she says her
head aches . . ."

I crawled out of my sleeping bag to go and have a
look at Teeny. It wasn't necessary to have a medical
degree to see what was the matter with her. You
could diagnose it without even being able to read.

"Heavens!" I exclaimed. "Teeny's got the mumps!"

"I'm not surprised," Agnes informed us, "because
Tove, her bosom friend on the third floor, had them
last week."

"I suppose we ought to turn back," I said.

"Certainly not," said Peter still snug in his bag.

"We're going south to seek a cure for the unfortunate
child."

The unfortunate child was not running a tempera-
ture. On the other hand I could quite well see how
we would be welcomed in camps all over Europe with
a case of walking mumps.

"No problem at all," said Anders at breakfast,
which we ate in privacy behind the wall of our tent.
It was still raining. "We'll just say the kid always
looks like that."

It was a hard test for a mother. I had always been
proud of my children turning out so well, and besides,
Teeny was the prettiest of them all.

"I do hope Berta isn't sick too," Benedicte said.
"She won't touch her food."

We felt Berta's nose, and it was as wet and cold
as it should be. Peter gave her a cup of milk, but she
didn't want anything.

"At least her head isn't swollen," Anders said.

While we were packing our gear Herr Aarslev
came by. He greeted me effusively, cast a covert
glance at Peter, and mumbled, "Tennis!" He let his
gaze pass over the unfortunate children who were
burdened with such a father. His eye was arrested by
Teeny's impressive head and awkwardly wandered
away. After that there was a kind of pity and forgive-
ness in his expression.

Herr Aarslev understood it all clearly now. A
family could be hit so hard by fate that it was unable

to take an interest in the important questions of the day.

He came back a little later with two bottles of beer, one of which he tendered to Peter.

"Prosit, old chap!" he said and put his bottle to his lips and laid back his head. But even in that position his eyes were fixed on the giant balloon that sat on my youngest daughter's shoulders.

As we were getting into our car Fru Aarslev, who had said we could call her Gurli, turned up. She, too, looked long and earnestly at Teeny; but her eye was caught by Berta who, wet and smelling evilly, was bedding down on the back seat.

"I wonder if it could have been your dog that polished off a whole dish of sausages belonging to Herr and Fru Schultze in that yellow tent over there?" she said. "The sausages were there when Fru Schultze went to call her husband. She stopped by for a morning snifter in our tent. But when she returned to her tent the dish was empty . . ."

"It couldn't have been Berta," I said. "She is very finnicky. She doesn't eat German sausages, that I do know."

Peter started the car and we waved to Fru Aarslev. We drove for five minutes, and then Anders said that it was nice to know that there was nothing the matter with Berta.

We reached the Alps the next evening. Friendly mountain-dwellers came and told us that not even their oldest people could remember a summer so wet as this one.

Nearly all the motor camps had been flooded out, but if we talked to the innkeeper up the road a piece, they dared say he would let us camp in his garden. Especially if we took our meals at the inn.

This sounded promising, especially as Fixy, the portable kitchen, probably wouldn't function with all the water that was still coming down in torrents. We had lived on cornflakes, bread and sausage, and fruit ever since we set foot on German soil.

The tents were like wet compresses, but we managed to put them up, and the inn people let us dry out the mattresses by the fire in the inn. Berta was playing at dog-of-the-manor, stretched out in front of the roaring fire, and Peter and I and our offspring sat on long, scrubbed, wooden benches and ate soup and pork and cabbage.

Teeny's head was still an object of great interest. Two old women crossed themselves as they passed by our table.

During that night at the foot of the Alps I learned how hospital patients feel when they are put in a wet pack.

Everything we had was wet. The tent, the ground-sheet, even the sleeping bags that had been warmed indoors. They seemed to suck water from the air.

During the night I dreamed that I was participating in the annual swimming race across the English Channel. Later the dream became a nightmare in which I had to drive the car across the Alps, and all the roads had become rivers and streams. When I woke up with clammy brow it was comforting to see Peter sleeping soundly by my side. Thank goodness one had a man to take the wheel over high mountains. Because I'm one of those people who can't even stand on a fifth-floor balcony without wanting to throw myself over the edge and get it over with.

The next morning the father of my children was unable to get out of his sleeping bag without help. He had developed a crick in the back and screamed like a wounded animal when he tried to get into the car.

We tried warming him by the fire in the inn and we managed to fold him together sufficiently to get him into the front seat next to me.

But I had to drive willy-nilly. And after all, what had I got a driving license for, if I couldn't take my family across a bit of mountain?—Peter wanted to know. My nightmare had come to life.

In his ravaged condition Peter balked at nothing. Berta was placed in the front seat between Peter and me, and all our clammy children in the back where Anders and the twins took turns at having Teeny on their laps. Her big head jutted up and prevented me from seeing through the rear window.

In my Latin textbook at school there was a dramatic

account of how Hannibal took his army across the Alps. But it fades into insignificance compared to what befell us when I made the same trip with a paralyzed husband, four children—one with a big head—and a poodle.

Considering the frightful pains Peter said he was suffering, his interest in my driving was really impressive.

"Go on, step on it—overtake that Volkswagen!" he would say. Or: "Now second gear—and have you remembered to release the handbrake?"

Or: "Is it necessary to keep so far to the right?"

Or: "Third gear, now . . ."

Thus encouraged I drove on ever onwards and upwards; and the steeper the road got the more doubtful I became.

"There must be something wrong," I said. "It feels as though the engine can't pull any more . . ."

Peter brushed my fears aside and referred to Johansen at the service station who had said himself that the spark was correctly adjusted. What this was supposed to mean Peter was unable to explain, but I could take it from him that if Johansen had okayed the car then it wasn't for me to cast aspersions on the engine.

Right in the middle of a very steep mountain road the engine stalled.

"Everybody out!" Peter shouted and remained in the car. "Now push, all of you . . . I'll . . ."

Never had so many moved a car so little. I and

the children and the dog finally moved over to the side of the road to take council, while Peter sat in the car and glared at the dashboard.

"It's the ignition," said Anders, my eldest son.

"Rot!" I said. "Johansen says . . ."

"It's still the ignition," my son insisted.

"Help!" Teeny screamed. "Daddy's going down the mountain!"

The child was right. The handbrake had tired of holding the car on the side of the mountain, and there it was, rolling slowly backwards taking Peter and his lumbago and all our baggage with it.

We jumped forward in a body and put our shoulder to the back of the car and shoved bits of sticks and stones under the wheels. There we stood, leaning against the car that wouldn't go to prevent it from running away, when a Volkswagen came chugging past our pitiful little family group.

It disappeared around a bend and came back five minutes later. It stopped and the driver presented himself and said that he was the owner of the restaurant in the pass on top of the mountain. "I'm the rescue party!" he said jovially. "It's sure to be the ignition. It always is. The only thing to do is to take it back down the mountain, turn it around, and come up backwards."

If there's one thing I know, it's my own limitations insofar as backing a car is concerned. Especially on narrow alpine roads.

"My husband is very ill," I explained pitifully, "and these are the four children—one with mumps—who are dependent on me. If I offered you ten marks . . ."

"It's a deal!" said our rescuer, and a moment later I saw our Taunus with all our baggage and Peter and the stranger disappear around the hairpin bend going backwards at breakneck speed.

An hour later my children and I were agreed that we would probably never see our car and their father again. I told my little flock that we might have to work our way home by singing and dancing in the market places and exhibiting Teeny's head and letting Berta do tricks.

It had begun to rain again, and we sat under a tree and watched cars go by, and every time we heard one approaching we picked up hope that it might be their father after all.

"Here comes a Danish car at any rate!" Anders shouted and jumped into the roadway.

"It's the Aarslevs!" said Agnes. "Their ignition appears to be sparking all right."

Herr Aarslev stopped and his Gurli climbed out to hear how things had come to such a sorry pass with us, our family dispersed and me a widow with four children—one ill—and a dog, reduced to living on roots and berries and the bark of trees near the mountain top.

"Of course it's the ignition!" said Aarslev from the car. "Men like your husband, ma'am, who likes tennis, are helpless in the hands of the mechanics. When I think of the tricks my brother-in-law Harley, who owns a car repair shop, plays on people who insist on having a car though they can't tell the difference between front-wheel traction and four-wheel brakes! It's their own damn silly faults—but I'm sorry for you and the kids . . ."

"Nice of you to say so, Herr Aarslev," I said. All of a sudden I felt very sorry for myself.

While the children and I stood there being pitied, I suddenly heard a hissing sound from the hairpin bend and the rear end of a light blue Taunus hove into view.

"Goodness gracious," screamed Fru Aarslev. "It's going the right way up the wrong way around!"

The car went by as if it had been shot out of a three stage rocket. The man from the mountain pass was at the wheel, and by his side Peter waved his arms frantically and yelled that they couldn't stop. We would have to walk up to the pass to meet them.

Herr Aarslev proved to us that his heart was in the right place. He said we could all pile in and ride up with him and Gurli.

"It can't be very far," I said, hopefully.

"I'm not so sure," said Herr Aarslev, "but jump in."

It took us ten minutes to get up to the inn where our car was parked in the yard. I judged that it would have taken me and my wet children at least an hour to walk the distance.

"Thank you very much," I said. "Will you let me offer you some refreshment?"

"A little snifter," said Fru Aarslev, "eh, Gunnar?" The Aarslevs had beer while I called to Peter and asked if it wasn't kind of the Aarslevs to have taken us with them.

"A little walk wouldn't have done you any harm," my husband said later, "but you always have to talk to everybody!"

Meanwhile Peter's lumbago had disappeared. It seems that, riding down with the inn keeper—who probably made a good thing out of cars that didn't spark right—Peter had explained that he was no ordinary tourist but an unusual medical case. He had—as far as his German permitted—described his sufferings for Herr Heinz, which was what the innkeeper was called, and had in him found an understanding and sympathetic listener.

Arrived at the turning-around place at the bottom of the road, Heinz had suggested that they go on another couple of miles to the village where his brother kept a café. He served a special concoction that was simply fantastic in its ability to cure lumbago and the like in back and limbs.

Peter is not the man to neglect trying any new

cure, and so they rolled on. Peter drank three of the aforementioned concoctions, and insisted in all friendliness that Heinz and his brother Hansi should also take the cure.

Peter assured me that Hansi, too, was a real pal and had expressed the deepest sympathy for Peter's suffering.

The drink he had concocted for them consisted of fifty per cent pure alcohol, Peter explained with eyes like dull pewter. Never before had a crick in the back been cured so expeditiously and so effectively.

I realized that Heinz must have possessed a stomach of a cast-iron lining since he had been able to thread the car up the mountain backwards after his libations. It was clear to me that Peter had not.

"If Daddy's lumbago is all gone why doesn't he drive the car?" asked Teeny as we drove away from the inn with Daddy on the front seat and Mother at the wheel.

"Your father is very tired, dear," I said.

Soon Peter fell asleep. When he woke up it was evening and we were halfway over the Alps. The alcoholic mists had lifted, but his lumbago had unfortunately returned.

It was therefore I who drove us into the very wet auto camp. We had hardly stopped before I heard Fru Aarslev's voice. She had collected the six Danish couples she had found there and had got up a sing-song. She herself was leading the choir which was rendering that sad old dirge, "Far from home, and no more beer—no more beer, and far from home."

While Peter groaned in his sleeping bag with a hot-water bottle I had borrowed from the man who ran the camp store, I listened to the mournful songs of my distant homeland that were coming from under the Aarslevs' tent.

As Fru Aarslev launched them into "See, the Summer Is a'Buzzing o'er the Meadow," my thoughts went out to my summer house in the bay of Koge, to the automatic hot-water heater, to our own little sky-blue toilet, and last but not least, to my bed. My lovely, big, dry bed.

Just before I dropped off I could hear that my children had joined their singing compatriots. The twins' pure voices were crystal-clear in the mountain air, singing "Roll me over in the clover . . ." which they had picked up with amazing speed. Teeny had stuck her harmonica in the front of her swollen face and was accompanying the singers. My children had obviously become the life of the party. What more can a parent hope for?

Just as I was about to drop off with my faithful Berta at my side, Herr Aarslev opened the flap and stuck his kindly, well-meaning face in.

"I thought I'd let you know that it was five to two," he said enigmatically.

"What was?" I asked.

"The match between Frem and Koge. The Jacob-
sens have a portable radio—so if you want to hear
the sports results and the concert tomorrow, you'll
know where to go. One likes to know what's going
on even if one is abroad, doesn't one?" added Herr
Aarslev huskily. "One mustn't forget the folks at
home, must one?"

"No," I said, and thought of Ellen and Henry and
their children, snug and dry in our summer house,
where the only sound was the gentle lapping of the
waves against the shore.

Next morning Teeny's head was down to nearly
normal, and Jacobsen's radio said there was sunshine
ahead. We rolled down the right side of the Alps and
found a place to camp where we could spread out
all our wet things and dry them thoroughly.

That day we tried Fixy, the portable kitchen, for
the first time. Peter was undoubtedly right when he
maintained that its capacity was the same as that of
a modern Danish stove, and that it would actually be
able to supply us with every kind of dish, from roast
pheasant trimmed with its own feathers, to fried eggs
—but only if one brought one's own cook-mechanic,
or if one could find the directions for use that had
disappeared in the wet confusion up north.

Peter sweated a whole morning over Fixy, the

portable kitchen. Every time he announced that it was now ready to go, it looked more like the surrealist invention of a mad artist than a camp kitchen. This wouldn't have mattered so much if Fixy had worked, but either we could not possibly get it to burn, or else it sounded as if it were getting ready to blow up.

Things weren't made any better by Anders' returning from the local post office bearing a postcard from Henry and Ellen. They not only told us about the wonderful weather they were having, but they described the dinner they had served for Henry's brother and sister-in-law. In my summer house kitchen Ellen had conjured up lobsters, fried chicken and strawberry-meringue cake.

Things came to a head when Anders in a superior tone of voice began to tell his father how he, Anders, thought Fixy, the portable kitchen, ought to be put together.

"We're never going to have anything hot to eat any more!" wailed Teeny. "And Mummy had promised me spaghetti, too!"

But we had hot food that day. Towards evening the Aarslevs' car rolled in, much to the delight of the children.

"Yoohoo!" called Fru Aarslev. Then she looked at Teeny, whose head was quite normal again, and asked if the child hadn't changed.

"Yes," said Peter. "We visited a holy spring . . ."

"There now!" said Fru Aarslev. "That's what I've

always said to Gunnar. There are more things twixt heaven and earth . . ."

"Well I'll be goddamned!" exclaimed Herr Aarslev, who had come up. He was looking at Fixy, the portable kitchen, with admiration. "That's a swell outfit!"

"Yes, but it doesn't work," I said.

Peter said he had just been looking at it, but explained that he had difficulty in leaning over because his lumbago was. . . .

"Here, let me!" said Herr Aarslev.

Five minutes later Fixy was working.

"You know what?" said Fru Aarslev. "I don't need to set mine up now. I'll make dinner here for all of us, and in half an hour there'll be a big surprise for everybody!"

The surprise was real Danish hamburgers with fried onions and bottled beer.

"If you only knew the trouble we have getting potatoes," Fru Aarslev said. "You can say what you like about the Italians, but they're not properly civilized!"

We had a wonderful evening. Herr Aarslev said he wanted to "stir his wooden leg," and the children went with him. Peter, who still hobbled about, preferred to go for a gentle walk with me, and besides we had Berta to think of.

While our offspring and our new friends went to the dance-restaurant by the auto camp, Peter and I and the dog went to a *trattoria* and drank Campari and decided that life was wonderful and that we were going to stay where we were until Peter was able to drive the car again.

It was one o'clock in the morning when we got back to the camp. The kids hadn't returned yet. We could hear the romantic music of an Italian band from the restaurant.

Shortly afterwards Herr Aarslev turned up with Teeny and explained that he had suddenly realized that it might be her bedtime. The others were having too good a time for us to expect them back until further notice.

Peter had just crawled into his sleeping bag and I had returned from the washing and bathing conveniences, when Teeny called from the girls' tent.

"Mummy, guess what? Agnes has got engaged . . ."

"Rot!" I said. "Agnes is only sixteen."

". . . to a very elegant Italian gentleman," Teeny went on. "He bought wine for everybody, and you ought to see how Agnes is carrying on . . ."

"What was that?" Peter asked sleepily when I returned to our tent.

"Oh, it's only a lot of rubbish. Teeny was saying that Agnes had got herself engaged to an elegant Italian . . ."

"Oh, well, good night," said Peter. Ten seconds later he sat straight up in his sleeping bag.

"What was that you said about Agnes?"

"Oh, you know what little sisters are like. It was only Teeny saying that Agnes had got herself engaged . . ."

In ancient books one can read many a strange tale of miraculous cures. But these all fade into insignificance in comparison with the miraculous transformation that in the space of one second took place in Peter's lumbago-ridden body. He jumped straight out of his sleeping bag and into his pants. His face was white as a sheet as he accused me of being a neglectful mother who could sit there and smear cream on her face while disaster was overtaking her child. Did I intend to throw my daughters to the men of Italy? This man might be a degenerate, a white-slave trafficker . . .

Peter shot out of the tent like a rocket. Ten minutes later I heard the twins' protesting voices.

"But, Dad . . . he only kissed Agnes' hand," Benedicte said.

"He was so nice," said Agnes. "He's got a car and he's going to take us for a ride tomorrow."

"He can take Fru Aarslev for a ride," Peter retorted. "I'll give you all the rides you need!"

"What was he like?" I asked when Peter had simmered down into his sleeping bag again.

"A wolf in sheep's clothing," said my husband, and that was all the description I could get from him.

The next morning Agnes sat like Lorelei and combed her hair for a full half hour. At ten o'clock a sky-blue sportscar with a young man at the wheel rolled up.

"Oh, look!" said Fru Aarslev, "there's Giovanni. He's come to take the girls for a ride."

"What a pity," Peter said, "because we're leaving now. We have to get to the Mediterranean before nightfall!"

Peter packed with such a display of energy that his lumbago returned. That was why I was still driving when we reached the auto camp on the French Riviera.

Agnes had been sniveling most of the day and had repeatedly told her father that she was going to leave home as soon as she could support herself.

"Isn't it lovely here?" we asked one another when we finally got to bed after having made dinner our-selves for the first time on Fixy, the portable kitchen. Even Agnes was almost her old self again.

"I miss the Aarslevs," said Teeny. "Herr Aarslev has promised to take me to the automobile races when we get home . . ."

Our day usually began with one of the children crawling into Peter's and my tent and telling us what the time was. For example: "Mummy, it's six o'clock already . . ."

But the following morning our first visitor was a large yellow dog of uncertain ancestry. It walked straight across Peter and me to Berta who stood and waited expectantly.

"Out with you!" said Peter inhospitably and flipped his hand at the yellow dog. It didn't seem to understand Peter's Danish, however, for it made a series of passes at Berta who seemed to be in the mood for visitors.

I was hit by an awful suspicion.

"I hope Berta isn't in heat!" I said.

"Oh, no!" Peter groaned. "Not that too!"

Another glance at Berta confirmed the awful presentiment. I managed to get the yellow dog out of our tent. It sat down and kept faithful watch six feet from the entrance, and later that morning received reinforcements in the shape of a terrier and a silver poodle.

They whined a serenade in their doggy French voices, so sad and gripping that we nearly went out of our minds. From time to time one of them would approach and lift a leg at our tent, and it was in the nick of time that we saved Fixy, the portable kitchen, from anointment.

We went for a walk with Berta through the town, and the band of worshiping canines was increased to five dogs, four of them of unorthodox extraction.

One of them looked exactly like my idea of a werewolf. He seemed to be Berta's special favorite.

When we returned to the camp we found that Anders had spent the time making the acquaintance

of a German blonde, long since out of her teens; while
Agnes and Benedicte were being photographed in
their bathing suits by two French gentlemen who
told us very politely that they regarded the girls
from a purely artistic point of view, because they
were so alike.

"Imagine!" said Benedicte. "Pierre says—Pierre is
the one on the right—that he may be able to get us a
job as models. He says there's money in twins."

Peter cast a glance at Pierre that could have frozen
the Mediterranean so thick you could have walked
across it to Morocco.

Personally I prefer to be practical, so I asked Pierre
and the other youth—whose name was Jean—if they
would care to give us a hand in catching the dogs and
removing them from the camp. There must be a
police station somewhere, I said.

Eager to make a good impression, Pierre set off at
a gallop after the werewolf, while Jean threw himself
into the middle of the pack, leaving me free to devote
myself to the preparation of our midday meal on
Fixy.

Pierre came back a little later and announced that
he had met the owner of the werewolf and returned
it, and that Jean had caught a dog too, and was on his
way to the police station with it.

It wasn't till after we had eaten our dinner and
collected a number of good bones for Berta, that we
discovered that she had disappeared.

Agnes sobbed that she expected Berta had thrown herself into the sea because we wouldn't let her marry the werewolf. She cast reproachful looks at her father who, in her opinion, represented the reactionary, Victorian element in our family.

Benedicte, who is more down-to-earth, thought that Berta had probably gone off with some dog or other, and now we were going to have puppies and they'd probably be born in the week when we moved from our summer house back to our second-floor apartment in town.

"Won't that be fun!" she said.

Anders—who is the family pessimist—opined that Berta had been stolen, while Teeny said with a sigh that she had probably had enough of life abroad and was now walking back home to Denmark.

We searched for Berta all that afternoon. Jean and Pierre and the German blonde tagged faithfully along, but I had a sneaking idea that it wasn't only for the sake of our dog.

Towards evening we arrived, tired and foot weary, in the market place of the mountain village. And there we found our five friends—the dogs that had accompanied us on our morning constitutional—but no Berta.

"Why don't you just take one of those instead?" asked the blonde. *"Ein Hund bleibt ein Hund!"* (A dog is just a dog!)

By this remark she lost forever all hope of winning Anders' heart.

"What is that place the dogs are besieging?" I asked, seeing them all jumping up and down and barking in front of the building.

Pierre explained that it was the police station.

I turned to Jean and asked him to describe the dog he had delivered at the police station that morning.

"It was a black poodle," he explained. "A most recalcitrant black poodle."

"Male or female?" Peter asked.

Jean hadn't the slightest idea. It was just a poodle, he said.

Peter made his way through the crowd of waiting dogs and entered the police station. A moment later we heard wild howls from inside, and then Peter and Berta appeared in the door and received the ovation from the family—and from the five dogs.

We bought a dictionary to see what chlorophyll was called in French, but the dictionary had been published before the age of chlorophyll. While human beings, according to the advertisements, become the center of interest at balls and on picnics if they have taken chlorophyll, the opposite is the case, we had heard somewhere, with dogs. They do not become the center of interest.

We were not successful in explaining to the local druggist what we wanted. When we pointed at Berta he showed us flea powder and a comb, and that was as near as we could get to it.

There was no alternative for it—Peter locked Berta in the car.

In view of the fact that Berta is a bed-and-furniture dog who has never spent a night away from us, she naturally didn't think much of the idea.

For several hours her howls made an antiphonal lament in concert with the yelps of her five admirers outside the car, and all the campers looked forward to a sleepless night.

Peter finally promised Teeny five francs if she would go and baby-sit in the car until Berta fell asleep.

While the band of love-sick dogs sat around our Taunus and lifted innumerable legs at lacquer and chromium, wheels and bumpers, five young men cruised about in the shadow of our tents in the hope of getting Agnes and Benedicte to accompany them to a temple of jazz in Nice.

Peter said unkindly that he was sorry Teeny hadn't infected the twins with the mumps so that they, too, could have had large heads. That would have solved a lot of problems, he said.

I thought the time had come for me to speak my mind. I explained to Peter that he seemed to be one of those men who are become old before their time, and do not understand young people, and who, what is more, do not understand their wife. I suggested that if he doubted his daughters' ability to look after themselves, he had better go with them to this jazz club. Incidentally, why shouldn't we all go instead of sitting there and listening to the dog-choir?

"Berta too?" Peter asked.

"Berta too," I replied.

Introducing Berta to jazz proved to be a good idea. The other dogs appeared to be averse to entering the very crowded and badly ventilated premises, where Peter and I sat and felt like decrepit fossils in the midst of the frantic noise, in constant danger from flying arms and legs.

As far as I can remember that jazz club was the only dogless place I saw from the morning when Berta turned on the heat until we set foot once again on Danish soil.

Introducing Peter to the world of jazz was not a good idea. After my remark about his outlook earlier that evening, he was eager to prove that he was as young and agile as his daughters and their young men. This he did to such effect that he sprained his wrist trying to toss Benedicte in the air while doing the rock-n'-roll.

Again it was Mother at the wheel as we returned to camp and were made welcome by four dogs.

"One of them is missing," Teeny observed. "I do hope nothing has happened to him."

We took Berta with us into our tent, and during the night both the werewolf and the big yellow dog tried to burrow under the edge of the flap. We took

turns at keeping watch and saying "Shoo!" every time the nose of a dog appeared under the edge of the canvas.

During the remainder of our travels our efforts were directed not at finding suitable auto camps but seeking out dogless regions.

Whenever we halted in a town to forage, a selection of four-legged would-be sons-in-law immediately gathered around the car.

When Peter and I and the children took a stroll in inhabited places, leaving Berta to howl in the car (the townspeople thought we were driving around with the Hound of the Baskervilles) we were followed by love-sick male dogs sniffing the odor of Berta's two-legged family.

We began to seek the solitude of desolate mountain places. I drove along tracks so narrow they had forfeited the right to be called roads, in order to get our harassed family to some remote spot where no white man, and no yellow, black, brown or spotted dog, had ever set foot before.

We reached heights where, I have no doubt, we would have been within our rights to plant the Danish flag. But the following morning would invariably find a dog or two wagging its tail outside our tent, and that would be the signal for us to pack up and set out for virgin lands.

In this way we saw Europe from a completely new

angle. There were dogs in front of us and dogs behind us. But Berta's virtue remained intact.

Our automobile, too, was still going strong, although I alone had driven it since Peter got his attack
of lumbago shortly after we had left Denmark.

But on the morning we left Hamburg for Grossenbrode, Peter thought that his latest injury—the
sprained wrist—was so nearly a thing of the past that
he would be able to take the wheel on the last lap of
our journey.

On the outskirts of Hamburg we barged into a
scooter being driven, so Peter said, by a monomaniac.
He, being German, treated us to a five-minute demon-
stration of the fantastic possibilities of the Teutonic
language.

A crowd of about two hundred had collected before
Peter and the monomaniac, after a final exchange of
injuries and visiting cards, made up their minds to go
their separate ways.

Outside our summer house Henry and Ellen and
their children were waiting in the warm summer
evening as we drove up to our little cottage with four
very dirty children and our camping gear in an in-
describable tangle.

"Everything go off all right?" Henry asked as we
sat and listened to the waves lapping on the beach.

"Just fine!" said Peter.

"No trouble at all?" asked Henry.

"Everything went smoothly," said Peter, "except . . ."

"Except what?" Henry asked.

"Except that I was unfortunately unable to drive for a short time. It's unnerving with a woman at the wheel."

"Yes, it'll never be quite the same with mother at the wheel," Henry replied. "As a matter of fact women shouldn't be allowed to drive at all."

chapter  ...

. . . which tells of the penalties of being public spirited, and how a nightmare can come to life in the middle of an intersection.

All in all I like my dreams. I know some people who spend the night having dreams that are as drab as neo-realistic movies in which all endings are unhappy; where the affairs of the too few protagonists invariably go wrong; where everybody is dressed in gray and the women wear unsuccessful permanent waves.

My dreams are not like that. My dreams are like Cecil B. de Mille extravaganzas. I dance the adagio from *Swan Lake* in the Hollywood Bowl while tens of thousands carrying flower wreaths cheer me and shout "Bravo!" I personally sing all the parts in the *Niebelungen* at the Metropolitan, and Maria Callas is my dresser. Everything I do turns out well in these dreams, which I usually have after days when my cakes have flopped and running my home has been beset with difficulties. It will be readily understood how enormously important these dreams are to me from the point of view of mental health.

In my store of dreams there is only one capable of denting my self-assurance. It turns up after I have

beaten Peter at tennis, or received top marks for one
of my children's school papers; in general, whenever
I get the idea that I am made for greater things than
being a wife and mother. This dream is just as extrava-
gantly directed as all the others. It always starts off
with my being engaged to play in an orchestra which
is being conducted by Leonard Bernstein. I am to play
the French horn.

Mr. Bernstein conducts a symphony and I sit and
blow out my cheeks and pretend to be playing.
Luckily no one can hear that I don't know how to,
while all the others are making so much noise. But
just as we are nearly through the last movement in
fine style, and the audience is beginning to notice the
good-looking lady who is holding the French horn
so elegantly, Mr. Bernstein points his loaded baton
straight at me. I have to play a solo.

Not a sound can I make. I blow and blow till my
head swells up while the color of Mr. Bernstein's
face gets darker and darker. The shame and scandal
engulf me and I wake up bathed in perspiration.

The dream can vary a little. I once played the
harp in Arturo Toscanini's orchestra, but that was
even worse. My fingers got caught in the strings. At
other times I have been entrusted with the double-
bass in a small, high-quality orchestra. But it always
ends in the same sad way with my being scorned and
ridiculed by both the audience and my fellow
musicians.

If I had been as wise as the ancient Romans or the modern psychiatry-mad Americans, I would have had this dream interpreted, and then it might not have come as such a surprise when my nightmare came to life.

The setting was different but there was just as large an audience as in my dream and it was even more frightening. Add to this that the nightmare became real at a moment when my power of resistance had been undermined by a series of nerve-wracking events which I shall relate in the order in which they took place.

It all began when Peter decided to demonstrate my public spirit. Peter had been playing cards one evening with our minister, whose name is Svendsen. Reverend Svendsen had worked out a plan for an outing for the old-age pensioners of our parish. They were to experience the delights of the Danish summer and see the sights of North Zealand, and he was rounding up motorists among his parishioners who could help him realize his project.

Peter always likes to help, so he at once put his car and his wife at the Reverend's disposal. "You can," he assured me, "learn a lot of wisdom from old people."

One summer morning when the weather looked ready for anything except sunshine, we all met outside the church. "We' consisted of ten motorized ladies whose husbands had shown how public-spirited they were by lending us to the Reverend, and fifty-two elderly ladies and gentlemen—plus the Reverend Svend Svendsen who seemed quite different from his usual self.

I know the Reverend as a gay fellow, fond of cards, a man who, like so many other men in our district, wears tweeds and a checkered shirt when appropriate.

But this morning he was in black, as was most of the flock surrounding him, and he held his head as though he were trying to get some bath water to run out of his ear. His voice was unctuous as he caught my right hand in both his and pumped it up and down.

"Welcome, you faithful friend, welcome indeed, and may the Lord bless you!"

"Hi-yah, Reverend!" I said as usual. As I said it I could hear that my greeting possibly wasn't right on the beam. But before I could get the chance to give my greeting a more spiritual twist he had turned away and was heartily pumping other arms up and down and handing out more blessings.

"Is my little flock all present and complete?" the Reverend shouted climbing the steps of the church. "Approach, my friends, approach, and let us all sing 'We will voyage into our Motherland' before we go out into the lovely land God has given us."

Our voices rose towards the gray skies. Four or five messenger boys on bicycles stopped and some

children on their way to school seized the opportunity to be late.

"It's a revivalist meeting!" one of the messengers shouted. "Make way for auntie—she needs a new pair of wings, too!"

I turned round to see who auntie could be and discovered that it was Ellen making her way through the crowd. Like Peter, Henry had promised his wife and his car to the Reverend. The lady chauffeurs were requested to stand in a row and receive their ration of old people.

"And for you," said the Reverend and looked me deep in the eye, "I have found four sweet old people. First there's Fru Blunt, one of the most faithful of my congregation."

Fru Blunt stepped forward and I gave her my best smile. She nodded stiffly and looked at my bare toes in my sandals. "We're going to have bad weather," she announced hopefully.

"No, no, Fru Blunt, I have prayed most earnestly for good weather," said the Reverend as though that closed the matter.

"And this is little Froken Jochumsen," the Reverend went on and shook a little more water out of his ear. "Yes, God bless her, this is little Froken Jochumsen!" he added and pushed a tiny little dried-out old maid forward. Unlike Fru Blunt she looked kind and cheerful.

"I *am* so looking forward to it!" she confided to me.

"I'm so glad," I said.

The Reverend had the next lady ready.

"I'm Fru Hansen," she said before the Reverend could say a word. "My husband died last winter. It's no fun being alone."

"No," I said, "I believe you. I hope we're going to have a nice day."

"It's sure to rain," said Fru Blunt triumphantly.

"Yes, but you heard yourself that the Reverend had prayed for good weather . . ."

"This is Herr Humboltsen," the Reverend interrupted. "Number four in your little band of passengers. Herr Humboltsen was eighty last Fall, but he's still hale and hearty and reads his paper without glasses . . ."

"I mostly look at the pictures," Herr Humboltsen declared, and stuck his elbow in my ribs and wheezed and said "pictures of ladies . . . you know what I mean? . . ." and he giggled.

"Perhaps you should let Froken Jochumsen sit in front because of her legs!" the Reverend called as I went towards the car with my four passengers.

I thought that would solve any problems as to how to seat my passengers, but I had reckoned without Fru Blunt.

"I want to sit in front!" she said when we got to the car.

"I'll be glad to sit in the back," Froken Jochumsen declared.

"You're the fattest anyway, Fru Blunt," said the Widow Hansen kindly. "There'll be more room for the rest of us that way."

Fru Blunt threw a black look at Fru Hansen.

"The reason I wish to sit in front is that I always sit in front in my son's automobile. Besides, Froken Jochumsen, being a dwarf, will be best off at the back."

"I'm not a dwarf!" Froken Jochumsen protested. "I may be small but I won't be called a dwarf!"

"Of course you're not a dwarf," I assured her, "Fru Blunt was only joking . . ."

"I never make jokes," Fru Blunt said curtly. "If I say Froken Jochumsen is a dwarf it's because she is a dwarf, and what's the matter with being a dwarf, if that's what the Lord has decided?"

"Some are big and fat and some are small and thin!" said the Widow Hansen and made herself comfortable next to Herr Humboltsen.

He was a gay little man.

"Come nearer—I like the ladies! I've been looking forward to sitting between two lovely girls!"

Fru Hansen giggled and Froken Jochumsen blushed. "I hadn't expected to sit next to a gentleman!" she said.

"We're lucky to have Herr Humboltsen with us,"

I said. Little did I know the trouble his presence would cause me.

Fru Blunt puffed and grunted her way into the seat next to me. "Can't the seat be pushed back a bit?" she asked.

"I wouldn't be able to reach the brake," I said, "and besides that will squash their legs at the back."

"I'm not used to riding in such a small automobile. My son has a Chevrolet!"

"Then why doesn't your son drive you?" Fru Hansen asked.

"My son is a very busy man. He doesn't have time for such nonsense."

"Well, really!" Froken Jochumsen said. "You can't say a thing like that to this lady when she so kindly has undertaken to drive for us."

"Well, she isn't a wholesale dealer is she?" said Fru Blunt. "I guess she isn't neglecting anything, and she comes along for the ride with the rest of us. By the way are you sure we're going the right way?" she added to me.

We were on our way out of town at the tail end of the other cars.

"Don't you think we should keep a little farther away from the other cars? I never trust the brakes on these small cars. The roads will be wet and greasy when it starts to rain. I knew some people who ran into the ditch in rainy weather. They were all killed except one man. He goes about in a wheel chair now."

"Relax," I said.

I noticed a sudden activity in the back.

I heard Fru Hansen ask the others whether they could smell the smoke. After that there were sounds as if somebody were searching for something.

"Is anything wrong?" I asked.

Complete silence.

Fru Blunt turned around with some difficulty.

"Why is Froken Jochumsen crawling around on the floor?"

"Herr Humboltsen has dropped his cigar," Fru Hansen announced.

"We're on fire!" Fru Blunt screamed. "I can smell it!"

I stopped the car. We recovered the cigar which had burned a small hole in the carpet, and I suggested to Herr Humboltsen that he give up smoking during the ride.

"You'll have to make do with the ladies till we get to Kronborg castle," I said.

"It's sure to be wet and slippery in the cellars under the castle," Fru Blunt remarked when we were on our way again. "I don't think I want to go down there. When do we eat?"

"Not before we have visited Kronborg," Froken Jochumsen announced. "I heard the Reverend say so."

"In that case I want an ice," said Fru Blunt.

I had to collect all my public spirit plus four kroners and purchase four ice-cream cones at the next ice kiosk we came to. It proved to be an unwise thing to have done. Fru Blunt got ice cream on her black moiré dress, and we had to stop at a gasoline station and wash it off. Fru Hansen felt seasick and had to be taken out and aired at Shipstone, and Herr Humboltsen dropped ice up his sleeve and had to get out and take his coat off before we drove into Elsinore.

We found all the others in front of Kronborg Castle. "How lovely the Danish countryside is on such a blessed summer's day!" chanted the Reverend Svend Svendsen. "To drive peacefully through glorious Nature!"

"It's going to rain in fifteen minutes," said Fru Blunt.

"I'm going down into the casemates with Fru Hansen," said Herr Humboltsen and winked at me.

The widow Hansen giggled and squirmed, and I asked myself if you could be sexy at seventy-three. It certainly looked like it.

"I don't want to go down into those horrible chambers," Fru Blunt announced. "It's sure to be clammy and slippery."

"Not at all, not at all!" the Reverend assured her.

"I'd rather go and see my niece. She's married to a haulage contractor near the market square," my front-seat passenger went on.

"But you can't go up there all alone," said the Reverend.

"The lady can drive me there. I expect she's seen the casemates before."

"Has Fru Blunt told you that she is the most

industrious of all the ladies in our parish sewing circle?" the Reverend Svend Svendsen asked gratuitously. "How many pairs of socks is it you have knitted for Danish sailors in foreign ports, Fru Blunt?"

"Eight hundred and thirty-five, and I've put a slip of paper with a bit of holy scripture in every single pair. My niece lives by the market, and we'd better be getting on if we're going to make it."

Fru Blunt acted on me like a snake charmer. I started to turn around slowly and walk towards my car.

"I expect she'll be surprised to see me turn up in such a small car," Fru Blunt opined. "You see all my family are well off. My son bought a whole new dining-room suite in the Renaissance style when my grandchild was confirmed. Do you have a dining room?"

"Yes," I said.

"In Renaissance?" Fru Blunt asked inquisitorially.

"No, it's modern . . ."

"Modern? I see. Well, you're still young. If your husband works hard you'll be able to buy one later. Take my son now . . ."

"He must be very clever."

"Yes. A pity he married such a slut though. She's a bitch," Fru Blunt declared.

"Good gracious!" I said, "you mean that she's immoral? How dreadful!"

"Yes, immoral, that's what she is. She wore a décolleté dress at the confirmation dinner."

"Yes, but apart from that, is she really immoral?" I asked and got ready to listen to some good scandal.

"She bathes in a bikini," Fru Blunt went on in a hushed voice. "And she wears sandals and paints her toenails red."

"Well, so do I . . . and I'm not immoral."

Fru Blunt wasn't the sort to hide anything under the seat. "Now that you mention it, I did think as soon as I saw you this morning that you were one of those like my son's wife. With red nails and a driver's license!"

"What's wrong with a driver's license? If I didn't have one I wouldn't be driving you over to your niece, would I?"

"In that case your husband might be driving," Fru Blunt thought, and proved that she had never met a man like Peter. I already knew enough about Fru Blunt to know that if Peter had been driving she would probably have been walking back to Copenhagen by now instead of being on her way to her niece who was married to a haulage contractor near the market place.

"You can wait here," Fru Blunt said when I stopped at the address she had given me.

"We have to be back in half an hour," I shouted, "so please return in twenty minutes."

Fru Blunt did not turn up twenty minutes later.

After twenty-five minutes I began tooting the horn. The niece who was well off came out first and glared at me. Her hair was full of curling papers and she had trodden-down slippers on her feet. Then Fru Blunt stuck her head out of a window on the first floor and said something I couldn't hear.

I tooted again.

"Didn't you hear me call that you weren't to toot the horn?" my friend Fru Blunt asked peevishly when she returned.

"Didn't you hear me say that we had to be back at Kronborg at eleven thirty?" I asked icily.

"It doesn't suit you to answer an old lady back," Fru Blunt declared. "Watch your driving! At that speed . . ."

"I've got to drive fast if we're going to catch up with the others," I said.

The Reverend Svend Svendsen looked annoyed and said that we must all help by keeping to schedule. And he gave me, not Fru Blunt, a steady look.

We divided the cars among us again.

Froken Jochumsen pulled at my sleeve from the back seat where she had installed herself quietly in one corner.

"I think Herr Humboltsen and Fru Hansen are still down in the casemates," she said.

"Off we go!" called the Reverend from his car.

"There's a couple missing!" I yelled.

"We all meet at the Nut Inn," answered the Reverend Svend Svendsen and stepped on the gas. The procession of automobiles disappeared leaving us behind.

Five minutes later Fru Blunt insisted that we go off and leave Herr Humboltsen and Fru Hansen. We would be late for the Reverend's short Devotion before lunch. People really must learn to be punctual, she said.

Froken Jochumsen would be happy to do without the Devotion if I would wait for the others. She volunteered to go and look for them. I thought of her bad legs and asked Fru Blunt if she wouldn't like some fresh air.

All Fru Blunt would like was to hear the Reverend. She had no intention of leaving her place in the front seat. So I climbed the battlements of Kronborg, Hamlet's castle, in search of the recalcitrant couple.

I found them on one of the bastions. They were standing hand in hand staring out to sea, the Widow Hansen leaning dangerously towards Herr Humboltsen.

"Come on," I said, "you'll miss the Reverend's Devotion."

"Time flies when you're with a lady," Herr Humboltsen explained, and Fru Hansen tittered coquettishly with undulating bosom, on which a plastic brooch bearing the words "Souvenir from Kronborg," was rocking.

"A present from Herr Humboltsen," she explained.

"Must do something for the ladies!" said Herr Humboltsen.

Later, as we were driving in perfect harmony towards Nut Inn, I heard the widow Hansen twitter "Don't, Humboltsen!" in the back seat.

Fru Blunt turned around. "What do you think your recently defunct husband would say to such goings on?" she asked.

"Oh, let them be!" said Froken Jochumsen. "We've come out to enjoy ourselves, haven't we?"

"It's no fun being alone," the widow Hansen said.

"It's delightful to be together with ladies," declared Herr Humboltsen who was quite insensible to the iceberg in the front seat.

At the Nut Inn, Fru Blunt trod on Froken Jochumsen's feet as they were tumbling out of the car at the same time. "That's what comes of not looking where you're going!" Fru Blunt said as she removed her two hundred pounds from Froken Jochumsen's toes and caught hold of Herr Humboltsen and asked him to help her up the stairs to the Nut Inn.

Through the open windows the Reverend's voice resounded. The Devotion was apparently still going on. But the Reverend's words did not pacify the widow Hansen. She followed Fru Blunt with her eyes as she hung on Herr Humboltsen's arm.

"The nasty old hag," she hissed. "She's going to try and steal him from me!"

"Mrs. Hansen, really!" exclaimed Froken Jochumsen who was still rubbing her left foot. "Herr Humboltsen is just being polite. He squeezed my arm in the car too."

"Oh, did he?" said Fru Hansen icily. "You don't say! Let me tell you that neither you nor Fru Blunt is his type. He likes a motherly woman. He said so in the casemates."

"In that case it's probably true," I said and took Froken Jochumsen's arm. The Widow Hansen went to the powder room and returned wearing lipstick. The color didn't go very well with her false teeth.

"She looks like the harlot of Babylon!" Fru Blunt proclaimed in a loud voice as the Widow Hansen sat down on Herr Humboltsen's other side.

I spotted Ellen and sat down next to her.

"There's nothing quite so charming as old people," my friend said. "I've got two sweet old ladies and two wonderful old men in my car. They are so happy and so grateful."

I wondered whether Peter had been rude to the Reverend when he played cards with him, since he had chosen my passengers with such refined cruelty.

"And now," said the stout churchman, breaking into my thoughts about him, "everybody is free to come and go as they like. We meet again at three o'clock. Go out and enjoy the blessed Danish summer!"

"It's going to rain," Fru Blunt interrupted. "It will be pouring down in ten minutes."

"Then you stay here," said the Widow Hansen and grabbed Herr Humboltsen's arm. "We're going out to the nut hedge."

I felt too old for the nut hedge. Instead I went into the bar and ordered a large brandy. When it had settled inside me things seemed a little less grim.

Outside the inn Froken Jochumsen was sitting on what looked like a very uncomfortable chair.

"Do you play 'Sixty-Six'?" I asked.

Froken Jochumsen looked all around her and said that she doubted if the Reverend would like to see us playing cards.

"He's a great card player himself," I said. "Don't worry about that. I'll go and rope in my friend and then we'll play a three-handed game of 'Sixty-Six.' "

Ellen is always ready for a game of cards, and we sat and played until it was time to depart. Fru Blunt suddenly appeared by my side.

"I shall have to tell the Reverend about this!" she said. "He goes to all that trouble to take us out into this beautiful countryside, and then you sit and play sinful games!"

"Amen!" said Ellen.

"That woman!" said Fru Blunt. "She reminds me of my daughter-in-law whom I was telling you about."

"In that case she must be very nice-looking," I said. "Didn't you know that my friend here used to be a famous belly dancer? By the way, Herr Humboltsen was asking for you," I said quite mendaciously. "Which way did he go?" asked Fru Blunt. "Down that way and then to the right. It's a bit damp there, but don't let that worry you," said Ellen. Fru Blunt disappeared. Froken Jochumsen won forty-six örer and was delighted. "It's thirty years since I had such a wonderful day. If my legs weren't so bad I wouldn't be so much trouble," she added.

That remark made me decide to fight to get Froken Jochumsen in the front seat on the way home.

When we were all called together I hurried along to my car to take a firm stance. I found the Widow Hansen and Herr Humboltsen sitting in the front seat. He had his hands on the wheel and was making buzzing noises like a little boy, and Fru Hansen sat close to him with a dreamy look in her eyes. They jumped up like two schoolchildren caught red-handed, and hurried around to the back seat.

This time it was Fru Blunt who was missing.

"Perhaps she's fallen in the lake," I said to the Reverend Svend Svendsen.

"Tut, tut, don't say such a thing!" he exclaimed. "The Lord will no doubt guide her steps." But twenty minutes later, and Fru Blunt still not returned from the blessed countryside, a certain nervousness crept into his eyes. He probably thought of the disastrous decline in the number of pairs of socks with enclosed bits of scripture, if Fru Blunt should have permanently disappeared from the face of the earth.

"You go to the right and I'll go to the left," the Reverend said to me. "That way we can't miss her."

I walked in the direction Ellen had pointed out when she showed the way to the two aging turtle-doves. In a clearing in the thicket I found her. She was sitting on a stub surrounded by various articles.

"Don't come near me, I'm not decent!" she screamed.

Her indecency consisted of having removed one shoe and stocking. They were lying in a very wet heap next to her. Here was a time when she could have made good use of just a single pair of the eight hundred and thirty-five pairs of socks, with or without built-in scripture.

"Rot!" I said unfeelingly. "You must come at once. Put the shoe on and come with me. There's a pair of my husband's tennis shoes in the trunk, which you can borrow."

"Never!" she said. "The Reverend must never see me like this."

"In that case you'll have to stay here by yourself," I said.

As we were shuffling along Fru Blunt angrily explained that she had caught a glimpse of Herr Humboltsen and the Widow Hansen on the other side of an innocent-looking meadow. Fru Hansen had been behaving with indecent familiarity towards poor Herr Humboltsen, and Fru Blunt had positively felt it her duty to come to his aid. Without thought for her own safety she had started out across the meadow, and it was not until she was up to her knees in mud that she realized that it was not a meadow but a marsh.

When I caught sight of my car it appeared to be empty. I came right up to it with the squelchy Fru Blunt before I discovered my three passengers down on the floor of the car, the Widow Hansen and Herr Humboltsen in front, and Froken Jochumsen in the back. The Widow Hansen looked as though she were ready to burst from spending so much time with her head down.

"The key has disappeared," she said.

"But that's impossible," I said. "I put it in the ignition just before I went off a moment ago."

"Yes, but . . ." Froken Jochumsen said and fell silent.

"Yes, but what?" I asked. "Has somebody taken the key?" Herr Humboltsen had two small red spots on his cheeks as he admitted that he had fiddled with the key. He wanted to show the ladies how one started a car, but at that moment the Reverend had come sailing out of the bushes. In sheer confusion he had tossed it away. And now they couldn't find it.

The Reverend Svend Svendsen came up and said it was regrettable that they had to wait for our car all the time. Now what was the matter? It would be too late to visit Frederiksborg Castle!

Froken Jochumsen began to cry. She had always wanted to see Frederiksborg Castle.

"Everybody out!" I ordered. I must have looked very fierce because Herr Humboltsen jumped as though for his life. He landed in the arms of Fru Blunt, who stood looking more sinister than ever with Peter's tennis shoes on. The Reverend and I turned out the car, he from the right and I from the left. He caught his finger in the slide under the front seat and I'm quite sure I heard him mumble "Hell!" The wind slammed the door onto my leg and I murmured something appropriate as his shiny face approached mine six inches off the floor of the car.

No key. "We'll just have to search you," I said. "Otherwise Froken Jochumsen won't get to see Frederiksborg Castle."

The Reverend Svend Svendsen looked as if he would personally like to blow up the Parish Home for the Aged.

With sardonic humor I suggested that he search the Widow Hansen while I did the same for Herr Humboltsen who was so fond of ladies.

"Now, now," said the Reverend. "Let us not be frivolous in this moment of trial."

"Will you look in your pockets, Herr Humboltsen?" he suggested. There was no key in Herr Humboltsen's pockets.

"Perhaps the ladies won't mind shaking themselves?" I said.

This proved to be an idea of genius. There was a little *pling*, and my ignition key fell to the ground. It had been cozily hidden away somewhere in the Widow Hansen's dress.

"I'm sure it's been down in her corset!" said Fru Blunt with disgust. "I wouldn't touch it with a pair of fire tongs!"

"It has not!" Fru Hansen cried in protest. "It was caught in the belt, I think. I once found a licorice drop there." She pointed to a place just below her diaphragm.

"Disgusting!" cried Fru Blunt.

"Shut up!" said the widow.

"Ladies, ladies, please!" said the Reverend Svend Svendsen sorrowfully.

Little Froken Jochumsen broke up the assembly by blowing her nose loudly. I took Fru Blunt to one side and suggested that she sit in the back. Because of Herr Humboltsen, I said. As far as I could understand he was disappointed not to have a chance to sit next to her.

"She can't sit here!" Fru Hansen shouted as Fru Blunt pushed her way into the back seat.

"Plenty of room!" said Herr Humboltsen jovially. "I'll just make myself a bit thinner. I love sitting with the ladies!"

With Froken Jochumsen at my side we drove towards Frederiksborg Castle.

When we reached the castle Fru Blunt refused to

leave the car. She wasn't going to walk about wearing Peter's tennis shoes and no stockings.

"People would think I was a loose woman!" she said. I failed to see what would make anybody think that. Loose women are known by many things, but not by varicose veins and big feet in down-at-heels, off-white tennis shoes. But I let Fru Blunt retain her illusion. She was probably enjoying it.

"It was very nice," Froken Jochumsen said when they came back from visiting the castle. "What a wonderful day we're having." The Widow Hansen clung to Herr Humboltsen's arm. They were both in such good spirits that anybody would think they had imbibed strong drink up in the Hall of the Knights.

"Like I was saying to Herr Humboltsen, it's no fun being on your own," the Widow Hansen chirped as she slipped into the back seat with Fru Blunt on one side and Herr Humboltsen on the other.

"You take up a lot of room," said Fru Blunt.

"Yes, but not as much as you," answered Fru Hansen. "Like I was saying to Frederik—that's Herr Humboltsen," she interjected triumphantly—"Like I said, it must be terrible to be so fat. Doesn't it hurt your legs when they are so fat? And all those veins!"

"Common people you meet everywhere," Fru

Blunt observed. "That's what my son says too. I saw at once that you were *very* common!"

"What a wonderful outing," Froken Jochumsen repeated innocently as we swung into the main road.

"We're going to have a cloudburst soon," Fru Blunt said.

"Frederik and I don't care," hummed Fru Hansen, "do we, Frederik . . . ?"

"You bet," said Herr Humboltsen. "I love ladies!"

For a long time Fru Blunt was silent. I think she was willing the cloudburst to do its stuff. When we had gone one third of the way back to Copenhagen she managed it. The heavens opened, the raindrops drummed against the windshield and across the hood, and all the windows had to be closed.

Just as I decided that Fru Blunt had lost the power of speech, she lifted up her voice again to announce that the Widow Hansen smelled.

"Now listen!" I said. "Let's call it a day, shall we?"

"Smell it yourself," said Fru Blunt.

I sniffed and had to admit that there was a strange odor in the car.

"Somebody must have trodden on something," I decided.

It turned out to be Herr Humboltsen who had an evil-smelling souvenir of a doggy nature from Fredericksborg under his right shoe. Now that the windows were closed the stench was unbearable.

"I don't feel so well," said Froken Jochumsen. "I'm so sorry to be so much trouble."

She was green in the face when I stopped the car and sent Herr Humboltsen out to clean his shoe.

"Mind you don't catch a cold, Frederik!" called the Widow Hansen into the rain.

"A good thing one can snuggle up to the ladies!" said the same Frederik when he returned to the back seat.

I have never before been so glad to see the Copenhagen skyline as on that summer afternoon. The rest of the trip had gone off fairly uneventfully, apart from the time when Fru Blunt said that the Widow Hansen had kicked her, and that other time when Herr Humboltsen had played his role as an octogenarian Don Juan to such a degree that he had tickled the nape of my neck, nearly causing me to run the whole party into the ditch.

Now we were in the streets of the city. The amount of traffic increased around us, and we drew near to the center of the city where the excursion was to end as it had begun, *i.e.*, with a song of praise in front of the church steps.

We were waiting at the intersection two hundred yards from the end of our journey, and I was working out that I could be home in a quarter of an hour, maybe twenty minutes, it depended on how long-winded the Reverend was going to be.

There were about fifty cars behind me, just as many

on the other side of the intersection, and a correspond-
ing number in the two other directions. I had to turn
left when the policeman who was directing the traffic
gave the sign with his white stick.

He lifted his arm and stopped the crossing traffic.
Now he waved on the cars that were going straight
across. And now—now—he pointed at me, and at the
head of a row of cars I rolled out into the intersection
to turn to the left. He was still pointing at me as my
car coughed and stalled with its side blocking the
traffic.

As if it would entice my recalcitrant car to start
going again, the policeman pointed not only at my
car but straight at me too, while cars all around me
tooted and hooted and bicycle bells rang and pedestrians yelled rude words and a tram clanged for all it
was worth.

The only thing that happened was that my face
got redder and redder, while Fru Blunt said she had
been expecting it all day, that it was a miracle something much worse hadn't happened, and ask Herr
Humboltsen if she hadn't said that morning that a
person like me had no right to have a driver's license.

The policeman's stick came nearer and nearer, and
now it wasn't the policeman any more. It was Leonard
Bernstein and the stick was his baton and I sat in an
enormous big French horn and had to blow it from
inside.

In the confusion Froken Jochumsen had rolled a

window down to tell the traffic-conductor that the car wouldn't go any more, and in through the window came the head of a messenger boy who wanted to know if I was going to camp in the middle of the crossing with all my grandmothers.

"Women!" he said disgustedly. "They should only be allowed to drive perambulators!"

At that Froken Jochumsen lifted her skinny little arm and slapped the messenger's face in a manner beautiful to behold and like music sweet to listen to. At the same moment the engine started up again.

I am unable to explain how I made it to the church-steps. "It's been a wonderful trip," said Froken Jochumsen as she took her leave.

"I knew the weather would be bad," said Fru Blunt triumphantly.

The widow and her Frederik disappeared arm in arm in the distance.

I sang "Brunhilde" that night at the Met against a background of five hundred Ziegfeld girls plus Josephine Baker wearing an ostrich fan. When I returned to my dressing room, where my dresser, Maria Callas, was humbly waiting, I gave her a hundred kroner and told her to go out and have a good time.

Next morning I woke up as good as new.

chapter VIII ...

. . . which relates how my son followed in Al Capone's wheel-tracks and of the dangers of turning an automobile —even for a short while—into an ambulance.

After our adventurous vacation abroad my feelings for our little house in the country grew even warmer.

When the children suggested the following summer that we roam the continent of Europe again, I put my foot down and stood fast. I explained to my family that I wanted a quiet vacation, a peaceful vacation, an idyllic vacation. A vacation with my own ground underfoot and my own solid roof overhead, a vacation in company with good neighbors that we didn't need to see too often.

This happened to be the summer when our son Anders became an undergraduate, and as a recompense for controlled diligence was given a driver's license by his father. It was that same summer and for the same reason that his proud grandfather made him a present of two thousand kroner.

"That will be a useful sum to have when you start your university career, my boy," said my father, who had seemed to become trusting in his old age.

Anders celebrated his exam with a series of student

binges. Had he intended to embark on a career as a brewer-examiner, the money would have been well spent. During the three weeks immediately following his graduation he became an expert on Danish beer. He talked weightily and with great confidence about the merits of the various products of a large number of local breweries.

Having in a short space of time invested five hundred kroner in these experiments, he decided that since the intensive study of beer led to nothing but hangovers, the rest of the money would be spent on something useful.

"A wise decision, my boy," I said with that warm feeling that my children had turned out well.

Anders' useful investment loomed on my horizon three days later. It tore a ragged hole in my peaceful summer. It made the very ground I stood on tremble. It made the air of our beachside residence reek.

Anders had invested in a very old automobile.

Peter and I and the children heard it for fifteen minutes before we saw it. It was one of those rare summer days that are made to laze in and get burned. Nobody had any energy for conversation; not even the birds sang, and the sea was still. Even Teeny kept her peace.

Then suddenly we heard a rumbling. It shook us out of our lethargy and into a discussion as to whether they were sending up a space-rocket from the military base a couple of miles along the coast.

Benedicte, who had been behind the barbed wire of the base on an excursion with her class at school, was able to reassure us that this could not be the case. She had seen for herself that the military equipment was of the vintage of the blunderbusses and crossbows that were distributed during the Napoleonic wars. The only thing at the base capable of rising into the air was a large gas balloon which was sent up twice daily on the end of a string with full military honors. Its purpose was to record the weather, possibly because the colonel had mislaid his barometer. One of Benedicte's classmates had asked if he might photograph the ascent, a request that had caused acute distress and a minor military inquiry. The officers at the base half suspected that the youth was a minion of the Kremlin.

The incident was closed, Benedicte explained, and the boy was allowed to leave with his classmates after relinquishing his photographic paraphernalia (an American box-camera of an estimated value of slightly less than three dollars).

From this apparatus the Defense Authorities, assisted by Military Intelligence, removed a film which revealed a series of interesting snapshots. There was a picture of two soldiers helping the colonel's wife hang up her washing. There was also one of a couple of men polishing two of the aforementioned blunderbusses, watched by the girls from the school; and a photograph of the colonel shaking hands with the children's teacher.

As nobody wanted these pictures from the life of the base to fall into enemy hands, the film was kept by Military Intelligence, and the camera was returned to the boy with the compliments of the Ministry of Defense.

Benedicte mentioned the story in order to prove to us that the welfare of the nation was in good hands, even though these hands were as yet unable to launch rockets.

While she was talking the noise grew louder. The neighborhood dogs began to bark and raise their hackles, while our own poodle, Berta, ran in and hid under the couch, which is her usual habit when danger threatens. She has no desire to be mixed up in anything that her intelligence cannot survey.

A couple of minor earthquakes were followed by a series of explosions, and then everything became silent. We rose from our bathing mats and went to see if the house was still there. When we reached the drive we stood face to face with the cause of the disturbance.

It was a 1926 Fiat and it was still trembling from its exertions. Out of it stepped a figure dressed in accoutrements that in many ways reminded us of a spaceman's get-up. The being wore dark goggles and was wrapped in scarves from head to foot.

The voice that issued from this mobile mummy was the voice of Anders.

"Boy, what a car!" he said and tore the goggles off, the better to cast loving glances at the collection of tin and old iron that stood smoking in our midst.

"Why are you dressed up like that?" I asked from the side of the drive.

"Dressed up?" said my son. "What's so unusual about me?"

"All of those wrappings on such a lovely day?"

"Oh, that's only because the windshield is missing," Anders explained and began to unwrap himself. "You can't have everything for fourteen hundred and fifty kroner, you know. But apart from that it's a beaut. Al Capone had one exactly like it."

I began to understand Al Capone's success. A ride down the street in a jalopy like the one standing before us would be enough to spread fear and terror among the bravest of the enemy gangs.

"Al Capone's was bullet-proof," Anders explained, "and the chrome moldings were made of real gold. But I don't think these are."

"No," I agreed, "I don't think so either. I seem to remember learning at school that gold won't rust."

As long as the car stood there looking highly explosive we kept a suitable distance. Later our curiosity won out over our circumspection. Even Berta crept near and sniffed at the plush upholstery inside the body.

"Real mahogany—can you beat that!" said Anders

and let his hand caress the wood fillets that kept the upholstery together.

He informed me that an imminent chore for me would be to wash the roller blinds, and that it would be the duty of his sisters to see to the renewal of cut flowers in the vases on either side of the missing windshield.

I would have preferred the car to have a windshield in place of some of the mahogany, roller blinds and vases.

When I mentioned this to Anders, he regarded me sorrowfully and said that he quite well realized that I was unable to appreciate the finer points of an automobile. One could always get hold of a windshield. The main thing was that there was a magnificent engine in the car. With a few repairs it would be the best motor in Denmark.

"Which repairs?" I asked, and saw in my mind's eye a bill for repairs several yards long from foreman Johansen, who now, it seemed, would be provided for for the rest of his natural life.

"It will cost millions," said Agnes who always seems to be able to read my thoughts.

"Rot!" said Anders. "Not when one has a mechanical bent."

"You haven't got a mechanical bent!" I reminded him. "You're just like your father. He can't plug in a reading lamp without short-circuiting the house. As though it wasn't enough that we have to send an almost new car to the shop every time the radiator needs water, you have to bring home a heap of old iron and plush that sounds like a bomb-attack and smells like a gas war . . . I shouldn't be surprised if it doesn't cause atomic fallout as well. Out it goes!"

Peter looked blank.

Anders lifted his hand to me in protest. His face was pale, and he addressed us in a voice of ice.

"One doesn't hit women and children," he said with dignity. "You may therefore insult me with impunity, although you ought to know that a man will put up with nearly anything—except criticism of his car. I should by rights leave home forever after the things you have said about my Fiat, but since we —despite everything—have had some good times together, I'll forgive you, mother. I'll forgive my sisters, too," he added magnanimously, throwing out his arms in an all-embracing gesture, "on one condition— that nobody goes near my Fiat. What was good enough for Al Capone should be good enough for you, too."

"I don't know what you are going to do," I said to my three daughters, "but I'm going to have a swim."

"Just a moment!" Anders shouted. "There's one more thing I wish to make quite clear: this automobile will not be a burden on the family budget. I have good friends who understand motors and who are going to help me take down the engine and give it a complete overhaul."

"May I inquire where this complete overhaul is to take place?" I asked. "Here?"

"At times you are quite intuitive," said Anders kindly. "The answer is yes, it will take place right here. We are going to make a start this coming weekend. Two of my pals are bringing all that's necessary on Saturday morning."

"Who are they?" asked Agnes. "Anybody we know?"

"They are some chaps whose friendship I prize," Anders declared haughtily. "You don't know them, but you'll see quite a lot of them in the future."

"Their names?" I said, "or is that a secret?"

"Not at all. One of them is Racetrack Robert. You must have read about him in the papers."

"No," said Benedicte, "we haven't. Has he been to jail?"

"He's a racing man," Anders informed us. "He was seventh in Malmo the other Sunday. It was in all the papers."

"And the other," I inquired. "Who is he?"

"That's Carl von Baumfelt. He's the secretary of the Alfa Romeo Club. A great guy. He's only twenty, and on his third car already."

"Where has he gotten three Alfa Romeos from?" I asked.

"But I just told you. He's Carl von Baumfelt!"

"You did, but that means nothing in my youngish

life, nothing that will explain three cars worth about eighty thousand kroner each."

"And you call yourself a housewife!" said Anders in disgust. "Don't you clean house? Don't you wash clothes? Don't you realize, that every time you drop soap-powder in water, it's money in the bank for Carl? His family is in soap. Any soap you buy, it's biscuits in the box for the von Baumfelts!"

"Does Carl make soap too?"

Anders' eyes reached for the sky.

"I just told you, he drives Alfa Romeos!"

"All the time?"

"When he isn't driving his Alfa Romeo, he's taking it apart," Anders explained in the voice of a long-suffering teacher trying to explain nuclear physics to the slowest pupil in the class. "He knows all about motors."

During the next couple of hours I pinned my faith on Peter. When he came home things would straighten themselves out. He would agree with me. He would remove the obnoxious reminder of Al Capone from our back yard.

Sometimes it is possible to consistently misjudge the man one has been married to for twenty years.

Peter's eyes lighted up at the sight of the Fiat blocking the drive.

"When I attended dancing school as a boy," my

husband said, "there was a girl who was brought and fetched in a car just like that. She had yellow curls and wore champagne-colored button boots."

"She wasn't Al Capone's daughter?" I asked.

"No, her name was Dora and her father sold dog food. He was also president of the Church Council."

"In that case she couldn't have been Al Capone's daughter," I conceded reasonably.

Peter suggested to Anders that they begin by removing the moldings and sending them to a place where they could be made to look like gold.

"Yes! And make the car bullet-proof, and have built-in machine guns in the upholstery and a hidden compartment for bootleg whisky," I said in disgust.

They didn't hear me. They were already vacuumming the plush furnishings which they had spread all over the yard. Later that evening I had to drive Peter to Doctor Poulsen to have five stitches in his hand, which he had torn trying to crank the car.

The doctor came back with us afterwards. He wanted to see the car for himself.

He helped them take off the moldings and put the seats back in, and he asked if he could come and watch when Racetrack Robert and Alfa Romeo Carl took down the engine.

Friday evening Anders said could we discuss the weekend arrangements.

"It's none of my business," I asserted.

"I was thinking of the eats," said my son. "Race-track doesn't eat fish or vegetables. Please remember that. I'm mentioning it just in case. But he doesn't mind sleeping in with me. Carl will have to have Teeny's room. She can bunk in with Agnes and Benedicte."

"No!" I said. "You can keep your guests to your-self."

I looked to Peter for moral support.

"Don't be a grouch," said my husband, who had let me down all along the line. "Of course Teeny can sleep with her sisters. It'll be nice for the twins to have two bright young men down for the weekend."

The two bright young men arrived on Saturday afternoon (a half-hour apart). Racetrack Robert's arrival was heralded by frightened screams as he came roaring up the track on a wild motorcycle with open exhaust and an uninhibited infernal combustion engine. Berta jumped clear by a hair's breadth as he braked in the yard, plowing an inch-deep furrow in the ground.

"Hi!" he said to Anders.

"Hi!" said my son and regarded Racetrack Robert's leatherclad figure admiringly. "This is Robert Dreves, mother," he said to me. "You've read about him in the papers . . ."

"Hi!" said Robert, and turned over the wad of gum in his mouth while he ogled Agnes and Benedicte.

"And the gorgeous chicks, whose are they?" he asked.

"They're my sisters," Anders explained.

"Hi—hi!" said Racetrack Robert with feeling.

He was big, red-haired, with close-set, pale blue eyes and dirty fingernails.

"Would you like to wash your hands after your ride?" I asked, making a brave attempt to be friendly and to make conversation.

"Nope," said Racetrack Robert.

"Before tea, I mean," I explained.

Racetrack Robert didn't answer. He had caught sight of the prehistoric Fiat and was emitting a long appreciative whistle.

He whistled again as he looked under the hood.

Anders' face shone like the sun and he sent me a triumphant look as I went in to put the kettle on for tea.

Carl von Baumfelt chased no children away as he drove up in his Alfa Romeo. On the contrary, he had a tail of shouting kids running behind the long, scarlet sportscar which, besides young von Baumfelt, contained two Pekingese dogs, a crocodile-skin valise, and a large case of tools. The car emitted a series of shrill blasts on what sounded like a twelve-tone horn, and Carl von Baumfelt stepped out while the neigh-

borhood kids gathered in an admiring group outside
our garden fence.

The two Pekingese tumbled out and nearly knocked
Peter's legs from under him as he rushed out to direct
the traffic in the yard.

"These are mother's dogs, Tristan and Isolde," the
latest arrival explained. "She didn't trust the servants
to look after them, so she got me to take them along
for the weekend. I'm delighted to see that you are
used to dogs," he added as Berta came running to
sniff at the additions to our family's animal population.

"Hello," I said. "I am Anders' mother. This is
Anders' father.'

"Yes, I thought you were," my son's guest
answered. "I'd better tell you at once that Isolde has
a weak stomach. She can eat only strained baby food.
I've brought some in cans. Will you be good enough
to remove any dishes with ordinary dogfood that
may be standing around? Otherwise she'll eat that
instead, and that will be most unfortunate for everybody."

"And how about Tristan?" I asked.

"Oh, he's perfectly normal in every respect."

"I'm glad to hear it," I said. "And yourself?"

"Thank you. I'm doing quite well lately, all things
considered. As a child I was very sickly and I still
have to be sure and get my rest and quiet, otherwise
I get nervous spasms around the heart. But so long as I
don't overdo it . . ."

He had a high-pitched voice and he was scraggy,

pimply and chinless. His blue blazer was unable to conceal his bottle-shaped shoulders.

"God save us from a couple of creeps!" Agnes muttered as she helped me with the tea. I suddenly noticed that the twins had put up their hair and donned their new beach suits. From the tone of Agnes' voice I knew that she considered that she had wasted her time.

We had tea surrounded by begging dogs and to the accompaniment of automobile talk.

Racetrack Robert had already had a preliminary hunt inside the Fiat and had come up with a sparkplug which he put on the tablecloth, and later, when he was through eating, on his plate. I wondered where he had secreted the wad of gum that had been in his mouth when he had sat down to tea.

It was a short meal. All the men—including Peter —were anxious to get out and dissect the Fiat. My question about the chewing gun was answered when I picked up Robert's plate and the tablecloth came with it.

One hour later there wasn't a square foot in the yard without some part of the innards of Anders' new acquisition on it. I would never have believed there could be so much inside a single automobile. Teeny came in with oil on her best bathing suit and the dog Tristan had to be bathed because he had strayed under what was left of the car. Berta had bitten Isolde, who took refuge under a bed which was too low to allow a poodle to follow, and young von Baumfelt had fainted from standing too long in the sun with his head under the hood.

He was stretched out on my best sofa looking very degenerate. His receding chin trembled as he related how he had gotten cramps as a child at the sight of an ugly nursemaid, and how his skin had since been a prey to impurities. "I do feel for the people they write about in the soap advertisements," he said.

"Haven't you tried some of your father's soap?" I asked.

"My skin is too delicate for soap," he shuddered. "I am obliged to use special creams. It's most troublesome. The only person who understands me is my dear mother. She knows that I can relax completely only with sportscars."

Through the window I could see that Racetrack Robert, Peter and Anders had dismantled the entire engine. I sincerely hoped that they could keep track of the thousand odds and ends that cluttered up our domain.

"I had so looked forward to taking that engine down!" young von Baumfelt said almost in tears.

"Don't worry," I consoled him. "I'm sure it will be just as much fun putting it together again."

"It won't be easy," said Carl von Baumfelt and

confirmed my worst misgivings. "Why don't you buy your son a proper sportscar, seeing that he's so interested in automobiles?"

I was just going to explain the difference between soap and the law and the comparative incomes they yield, when I was distracted by the blade of a knife flashing past my nose. Its handle was in Racetrack Robert's hand.

"Haven't you got one that's more pointed than this?" he asked. The knife he held in his hand was one of my favorite kitchen tools.

"Only the carving-knife, and that's not for the use of mechanics," I said pointedly.

"Was that a long, thin one with a curved handle?" Racetrack Robert asked. "I expect that's the one we've just broken. Haven't you got a better one than this?"

"You must take better care of your tools!" I shouted angrily to Peter who, dirty and happy, was getting in the way wherever he could.

"Now don't be so unimaginative!" my husband replied. "Surely it's in everybody's interest that we make a good car of it?"

When the team of mechanics stopped work outside they brought a collection of parts into the house and, in the course of the evening, cleaned them in the kitchen sink. I had to cut off Berta's whiskers which got covered with grease when she tried to eat some cotton-waste. Carl von Baumfelt wrapped up Tristan in two of my best bath towels because he said that the dog's fur was still damp from his afternoon bath. "My dear mother will never forgive me if Tristan catches cold," he said. "Next to me she loves the dogs more than anything in the world."

Racetrack Robert had fallen asleep in a chair after the day's exertions. His nails were even blacker than when he arrived. Peter, Anders and von Baumfelt discussed engines and racing records.

"I can't understand why people don't buy an Alfa Romeo right away," von Baumfelt declared, rubbing the dog in my bath towels.

Berta sat minus whiskers and growled in the direction of Peter's room where Isolde had taken up residence under the bed.

It began to look like a not too restful weekend.

Next morning, while I was setting the house in order, before my family and guests got up, I found more of Racetrack Robert's chewing gum parked under the edge of the table when I tried to move it. It stuck between two of my fingers. I tried to remove it as best I could with some of the alcohol that had been poured over the spare parts from the engine, after which I went to the bathroom to wash. I found the door locked.

I used the kitchen sink and went ahead with preparation for breakfast. Peter came in a little while later and asked who was occupying the bathroom for the last forty-five minutes. I suggested that he make a round of the bedrooms to see if any member of our temporarily swollen household were missing. He came back later and said that Racetrack Robert seemed to have disappeared.

"In that case I quite understand," I said. "It will take him all day to get clean."

The members of my family took turns washing in the kitchen sink, thus making my morning chores that much less simple. Carl von Baumfelt came out of his room wearing a stunning bathrobe made of turquoise-colored velour. In his arms he carried the dogs and all his pots of cream. When he discovered that the bathroom door was locked he looked very distressed.

"Your friend Robert is washing," I explained. "He has been using soap for a solid hour. Lucky you . . ."

"Impossible!" said von Baumfelt. "I know him. Robert has never washed a whole hour in his life. He wouldn't dream of wasting that much time."

"Perhaps he's sick?" I suggested.

We began calling Racetrack Robert. At first we knocked diffidently and called out in moderate tones of voice. Finally we banged the door and yelled in loud chorus.

That did it. Racetrack Robert opened the door and revealed himself to our anxious little band in the

passage outside. A glance reassured us that all was as before—apart from the pile of Teeny's Donald Duck comics he was clutching in one black hand.

"Hi!" he said.

"We thought you had drowned," I announced.

"Nope!" said Racetrack Robert. "I've been sitting here reading. The best thing about the morning is that you can sit in peace and read comic books."

I am no technician and I shan't attempt to describe all that happened to the old Fiat that Sunday morning. The only thing I knew for sure is that there was practically nothing left in the house I could call my own.

All the bowls and basins and housewares had migrated out to the desiccated car, from my floor bucket to my best mixing bowl, from my brushes to my vacuum cleaner.

Doctor Poulsen came to see how the work was getting on. He didn't leave again before his wife had rung up three times to remind him about a sick patient awaiting his pleasure in the next town.

Peter, who had promised to fetch some strawberries from a farm three miles inland, was deaf to all entreaties. And the entrance to our garage was completely blocked by automobiles and spare parts, making it impossible for me to get our own car out.

I considered whether I should ask von Baumfelt to lend me his Alfa Romeo. I was just about to do so when I discovered that he had begun to take it apart.

"He does that every Sunday," Anders explained.

That was how things stood when I came out later to call the toilers to Sunday luncheon. As I emerged from the door a fat little man came waddling up the drive. He was wearing Bermuda shorts and leather belt and a wrist-watch, and that was all.

"Pardon me," he said, "my name is Makkedam. Do the dogs bite?"

Berta, Tristan and Isolde had gathered around him and were sniffing at his hands with interest.

"I expect that's because I have been frying hamburgers," he explained. "Like I said, my name is Makkedam. I've just bought the white house over there on the other road."

"How do you do, Herr Makkedam?" I said. "Is there anything I can do for you?"

"Have you got any small children?" asked Herr Makkedam.

I showed him Teeny and said she was the smallest I could supply on such short notice.

Herr Makkedam's Adam's apple began to go up and down agitatedly. It looked as though he had a tiny, busy elevator in his throat.

"It's about an inquiry," he explained.

"Yes, Herr Makkedam?" I said expectantly.

His Adam's apple took another trip.

"I'm here to ask," he said, "if any of your children has called my wife a walrus?"

"A what?" I asked.

"A walrus," repeated Herr Makkedam more firmly this time. "It's supposed to have happened like this: My wife is bathing out at the second sand bank and she crawls up on the diving raft. Some children tip over the raft and my wife falls in the sea. When she reproaches the children for their behavior, one of them, a girl, yells out that she, my wife, is an old walrus. My wife is very indignant."

"It can't have been any of mine," I said. " Teeny has only been in once today, and that was with me."

"Who do you think it can have been?" asked Herr Makkedam with a despairing look.

"There are so many children on the beach," I replied. "It's difficult to say which one called your wife a walrus."

"I've been to nearly all the houses and asked. Are you sure you don't have any more children? My wife is very upset. I promised I wouldn't come home before I had found the guilty party. It was a girl wearing a smooth, light blue bathing cap."

"Herr Makkedam," I said easily, "all my children have white bathing caps."

"I see," said Herr Makkedam. "In that case I must apologize. Do you know whether there are any children in the house next door?"

"No," I said, "there are no children there, and none in the house after that either. You must be tired. And you're sunburned. Don't you think you should go home?"

Herr Makkedam was no longer listening to me. He had caught sight of Anders' car and the activities going on around it.

"I say!" he exclaimed. "What a wonderful old car!"

A moment later he was holding a wheel while Racetrack Robert performed a minor operation on the rim.

Long after the rest of us had gone in to lunch, the fat little man wearing shorts, belt and wristwatch, was wandering about and fiddling with all the loose parts that were still lying around. This was probably the time when some of the screws became interchanged so that neither the Alfa Romeo nor the Fiat could be put together again before foreman Johansen had been called. He came and for three hundred kroner he did the sorting out and putting together that made the cars exactly as they were before.

Monday morning, just before going back to town, Carl von Baumfelt went down to the beach for a dip. I met him out at the raft. He looked small and delicate in a bathing suit and he was wearing a light blue bathing cap, the only one I had seen on the beach that summer.

The next couple of days I thought a lot about Fru Makkedam. When one owns a husband who refuses even to fetch strawberries when you ask him to, it is natural for a wife to bow in admiration before a woman who is capable not only of getting her husband to fry hamburgers on a Sunday, but who furthermore possesses the power to make him go from house to house on a hot afternoon asking who has called her a walrus. Peter might conceivably—when a direct physical attack on one of his children is brought to his attention—get out of his deck chair, but not before I have caught the guilty party and dragged him up to Peter's chair.

When I derisively told Peter about Herr Makkedam's errand he became deadly serious.

"You should never laugh at such a man," he said. "He works and slaves all week in order to be able to send his family out of town during the summer. He arrives on Saturday looking forward to a peaceful weekend, and then at lunch-time, the sacred hour created to enable a man to sit down to a well-laid table, he is forced to carry out the unenviable task of going from house to house on an errand of non-peace. His wife must be a very beautiful woman to wield such power over him."

After that Peter began to speculate about the beautiful Fru Makkedam. He conjured up a mental picture of himself floating peacefully out near the raft and colliding with a beautiful blonde, a cross between a siren and a mermaid, a dangerous beauty, a single glance from whose eyes had the power to make a man do foolish things.

His dream did not materialize. Despite the fact that he frequented the waters around the raft with great diligence during the week that followed, he only met up with middle-aged ladies and splashing children.

I was the first to set eyes on Fru Makkedam. One peaceful morning when Peter had gone up to town with Anders and the children were on the beach with the dog, I heard somebody calling for help out in front of our house.

I looked out and saw a lady wearing a flowery beach dress which revealed a great deal that had been better hidden. She screamed at the top of her strident voice and her features left me in no doubt as to who she was. She looked so much like a walrus that I was tempted to throw her a fish.

"My dear Fru Makkedam!" I called. "Whatever is the matter?"

"How do you know who I am?" she asked suspiciously.

I began to give a vague explanation about having seen her on the beach, but she was already launched on the sea of her own troubles. It appeared that her poor little boy had been bitten.

"By what?" I asked and hastily reviewed the neighborhood dogs in my mind.

"By my hired girl!" screamed Fru Makkedam.

"That woman has always been after the boy, I've said to my husband time and time again that she looks treacherous. And now she's bitten him! I must get him to the hospital quick. There's a nasty long gash."

"How awful!" I said.

"Come dear," called Fru Makkedam. "The lady will drive us!"

This was the signal for an unusually ugly, fat, slobbering little boy to appear in the road.

"My husband has the car," I explained. "But I'll call you a taxi by phone."

"But you have a car!" said Fru Makkedam accusingly and pointed at the Fiat which Anders had left in the yard.

"Yes, but I can't drive that, it's my son's," I explained.

"Come, come!" said Fru Makkedam. "Do you refuse to help a child in distress? Show the lady your bandage, Benny dear."

Benny dear stuck his arm forward and sniffed and I paled at the sight, for quite a lot of blood really had oozed through the handkerchief that had been wrapped around the upper part of his arm.

"How dreadful!" I said inanely.

"The darling has bandaged himself. He wrapped his handkerchief around it himself after it had happened," his mother explained.

I looked from the wee darling to the fearful Fiat.

"I don't know how to drive it," I insisted. "There's no reason for more people to get hurt."

That worked. For the first time Fru Makkedam appeared to be amenable to reasoning. I seized the opportunity.

"I'll go and phone for a taxi," I said.

I was halfway to the door when matters took a turn for the worse.

"I wanna go in *that* car!" yelled Benny in a voice which showed that he couldn't have been wounded as much as we had thought.

"Did you hear what the child said?" Fru Makkedam called after me. "The little lamb wants so much to go in that car."

"But—" I said weakly.

"You can drive it if you want to!" decided Fru Makkedam. "Come, mother's boy!"

With these words she climbed up and took her seat on the plush-upholstered back seat, from which she stared down at me with eyes that revealed to me the power she wielded over her husband. I felt like a rabbit under the gaze of a boa constrictor. I approached the car hesitantly and placed one foot on the running board next to the driver's seat.

"Let's get going before the child bleeds to death!" screamed Fru Makkedam hysterically.

I found myself sitting behind the steering wheel. The key was in the ignition and I turned it willy-nilly. To my great relief nothing happened.

"There, you see!" I said over my shoulder. "I don't know how to start it."

"You have to use the hand throttle!" Benny hooted.

"I know nothing about throttling," I said coldly.

The suffering child thrust his arm with its bloody handkerchief past me and moved a gadget under the steering wheel which I had taken for the whatsit that sets the blinkers going.

The automobile began to shake and make noises.

"Now the gears!" Benny commanded. I twisted the lever in the floor and hundreds of teeth were ground and gnashed somewhere under the floor.

"Blop!" said the engine and died.

"Idiot!' said the patient on the back seat. "You must double-declutch."

"The boy's a mechanical genius," asserted his proud mother. "Do like Benny says!"

To my chagrin I found that Benny was right. I accelerated with hands and feet, double-declutched, and finally located first gear which turned out to be situated at a very strange angle.

Suddenly the car began to move. As I let go of the hand-throttle there was a mighty explosion from the exhaust.

We were on our way.

"Faster!" rooted Fru Makkedam. "We must get there before the child passes out!"

Something told me that it would take more than a bite in the arm to do away with Benny.

"Tell me, old pal," I shouted when we were out on the high road, "how did you happen to get hurt?"

Benny buttoned up his mouth tight.

In the rear mirror I could see that he scowled at me suspiciously.

"Is it really true that the lady bit you?" I insisted.

For one second Benny's eyes met mine in the rear mirror, and then he turned to his mother and began to howl.

Fru Makkedam caught hold of my shoulder and shook it. "Are you out of your mind, woman, to mention a happening that has already made dreadful scars in his little soul!"

"You must realize," I said to her, "that the hospital will have to report the matter to the police when the doctor learns what has happened."

"And quite right too!" decided Fru Makkedam. "I hope they put Fru Gormsen in jail!"

Fru Gormsen would be the biting lady.

We created quite a stir on our way as we sat there, an unholy trinity on its way to the casualty ward. Every time I turned a corner I had to catch hold of the hand-throttle in order to double-clutch, and every time I let go the little lever again it sounded as though I fired a cannon ball from the exhaust pipe.

When we reached the town and rounded its numerous corners, people came running out of their houses. I suspect they thought the Queen had at last given birth to a son and cannonades were being fired in the streets.

"Here we are!" I announced as we drew up in front of the hospital.

Mother and child stepped out, and with that I thought my mission was at an end. But no.

"You'll have to go with him to the casualty ward," she said. "I can't stand the sight of blood! In the meantime I'll go and see the police myself."

I was about to protest, but a glance at Benny showed me that he really was beginning to look very pale.

"A child in distress!" said his mother as though she could read my thoughts.

Fru Makkedam went off to seek out the police authorities, and I went in search of the casualty ward with Benny. There were at least twenty people in the waiting room. Next to the door a battle axe sat at a table and noted down names and asked questions.

When I explained to her that the little boy here present had been bitten by the woman hired to help clean the house, I could see that this was by far the most interesting case she had come up against for a very long time.

Benny stood and stared at the floor while I passed on the information his mother had given me, while everybody in the waiting room listened.

"Pardon me," said the battle-axe, "who did you say has bitten him?"

"The hired help."

"One moment please!" said the lady and looked at me strangely. She then disappeared through a door.

At the same moment I discovered that Benny had disappeared. I heard the door to the passage bang to behind him and the sound of his quick steps along the tiled floor.

"After him!" a man shouted. "He's got hydrophobia!"

Two patients, who a moment before had appeared to be dying, jumped up and set off after the boy.

As they passed a hospital orderly they shouted to him to follow them. The hospital was filled with clattering feet and excited shouts.

Everybody who was able to walk or even creep left the waiting room benches, either to follow behind the vanguard or to take refuge in the toilets. This last group consisted of people whose fear of rabies was greater than their curiosity.

From the wards came patients and nurses. Out of the casualty ward came the battle-axe followed by a tall, weedy man with a mirror on his forehead and a white coat on his wasted frame—looking like a refugee from a laxative ad.

Returning from the hospital garden at that moment came the orderly and the two men who had been in the vanguard of the chase, clutching a kicking Benny between them. The handkerchief had slipped down and the bloody wound on his arm was plainly visible.

"Watch out he doesn't bite!" shouted a woman with great tampons of cotton wool sticking out of her ears. She jumped up on a bench as the procession went by.

"Carry him in here," directed the doctor with the mirror.

The three men and Benny disappeared into the inner sanctum.

I sat down exhausted next to the lady with the tampons. She moved a little farther away, but that didn't prevent her from giving me an exhaustive description of the ailment behind the tampons. I also had described to me two complicated cases of abdominal trouble and one case of eczema. We were just about to have a run-down on a most complicated case of intestinal trouble, when the door opened and the battle-axe appeared.

"You, there!" she said. "Will you come in here?"

I looked around to see who 'You there' could be, and I realized from the way everybody was looking at me, that it was I.

When I once more came face to face with the doctor of the casualty ward he no longer looked like an advertisement for constipation. He looked murderous.

"How dare you!" he shouted and ground his teeth with a noise like the one I had made when I couldn't find the Fiat's clutch. "All my life I have fought for science and humanity, and then a crazy dame like this comes and . . ."

I caught sight of Benny who was standing jammed into a corner and scowling worse than ever.

"Your horrible child has made a mockery of this hospital, he has created a grave disturbance among sick people, he has jeopardized their health and lives . . . This little joke will cost you dear, I promise you!"

I looked around me. The battle-axe was standing guard by the door. A nurse was toying with a scalpel. The doctor, pale, the corners of his mouth wet, continued his monologue. I wondered whether the creepy company would do away with me then and there, smuggle my body down to their private morgue and sell my skeleton to medical students. Where else do they get all those skeletons from, I thought.

The only thing I desired to know before I should die was what it was all about. What had I done? What was my crime?

The doctor turned half around, poured a glass of water from a pitcher and drank it noisily. I seized my chance while he was still swallowing.

"Excuse me," I said, "but what is it you are accusing me of?"

"Accusing you of?" shouted the frenzied man. "Accusing you of? Ha! You come in here with an improbable story about a boy being bitten by a woman, and then it turns out to be a scratch—he has admitted it—that he acquired on the fence when he was on his way in to steal the neighbor's strawberries. You drag this mendacious child in here and upset the whole hospital . . ."

"But," I said, "the boy isn't . . ."

I didn't get time to disown Benny. The door was flung open and Fru Makkedam stood on the threshold.

"Where is my poor child?" she shouted and came in like a whirlwind. She was at once very bare and very flowering in her beach dress.

"Are you in charge here?" she barked.

She pointed at the doctor who opened his mouth to speak. He obviously didn't know Fru Makkedam when she had something to say.

"*I* am talking!" she said. "The police told me to say that they must be notified through the casualty ward. You must inform the authorities immediately that my son has been bitten by this cowardly woman, this . . ."

At this point I managed to get the door silently open. I slunk noiselessly out behind the secretary who appeared to have forgotten my existence. Fru Makkedam was still talking as I closed the door softly behind me. I was nearly through the waiting room when voices from the inner sanctum told me that the doctor was speaking again. Never—before or since— have I heard a single human being yell so loudly.

I found a small crowd of friendly people gathered around the Fiat when I returned to the parking lot.

I stepped up into the car, fired a salute at the hospital, and left town by the shortest possible route.

My teeth chattered all the way home, fits of shivering racked my martyred body and tears ran down my cheeks.

Having put back the noisy, shaking Fiat, I dragged myself into the bedroom, crawled into bed, and pulled the eiderdown up over my head.

Peter came and inquired about my health when he returned from town. Mostly because he wanted to know when I was going to get up and cook dinner. He reminded me that my parents were coming.

While I dressed I heard Peter's complaining voice from the living room. When I came in he turned to me and explained that he had reluctantly been obliged to tell Teeny off for telling stories and relating half-digested gossip.

"I wish to live in peace with my neighbors," my husband said, "and here she comes and tells me an improbable story about a big brick layer chasing Herr Makkedam because Fru Makkedam had said that the brick layer's wife had bitten her son. It should be beneath anybody's dignity to listen to such stories when one is thirteen years old, let alone believe them. And one should certainly not repeat them!"

"By the way, I've met Fru Makkedam," I said.

"What was she like?" Peter asked with interest.

I told Peter everything that had happened to me that day, from the moment I heard Fru Makkedam screaming outside, until I escaped from the casualty ward.

Peter listened with a serious face. When I finished at last I waited for him to clasp me to his breast in silent commiseration, stroke my hair in sympathy, and in his heart swear revenge on the group of people who had misused and offended his wife so grossly. But all he said was:

"All this could not have happened if you had listened to good advice while there was still time."

"What advice?"

"That women should leave automobiles alone!"

My aging parents were standing in front of Anders' Fiat, which appeared to be the sensation of the year in our part of the world.

"Well I never!" my father said with respect. "Have you notified the National Museum about this relic?"

My mother was silent. She walked slowly round the car, and when the rest of us went into the house she remained behind. From the kitchen I could hear Anders tell his grandfather how I had pinched his car that day.

"Never let a woman drive your car, my boy," said my father. "Nothing good ever comes of it."

I sent Teeny out three times to call my mother, and we were already at the table when she finally dragged herself away from the car.

She came in through the French doors, her eyes shining green and her hair golden in the light of the evening sun. Her voice sounded youthful and seductive.

"Harald," she said softly to my father. "I want a driver's license again!"

My father rose from his place at the head of the table, laid down his knife and fork with a crash, glared around the table and then centered his glance on my mother.

"No!" he roared.

He sat down again and continued eating. Peter and Anders lifted their glasses to the old gentleman.

It was as if in silent homage to the last man on earth who was master of his own car.